THE ORIGINS OF MAN

IS VOLUME

29

OF THE

Twentieth Century Encyclopedia of Catholicism

UNDER SECTION

III

THE NATURE OF MAN

IT IS ALSO THE

5TH

VOLUME IN ORDER OF PUBLICATION

THE TWENTIETH CENTURY ENCYCLOPEDIA OF CATHOLICISM

Edited by HENRI DANIEL-ROPS of the Académie Française

THE ORIGINS OF MAN

By NICOLAS CORTE, pseud.
Cristiani, Leon

Translated from the French by ERIC EARNSHAW SMITH

HAWTHORN BOOKS · PUBLISHERS · New York

First Edition, November, 1958

CUM PERMISSU SUPERIORUM O.S.B.

NIHIL OBSTAT

Johannes M. T. Barton, S.T.D., L.S.S.

   Censor Deputatus

IMPRIMATUR

✠ Georgius L. Craven

   Epis Sebastopolis, Vicarius Generalis
Westmonasterii, die XXX JUNII MCMLVIII

CONTENTS

PREFACE

This book begins the section in this series which is entirely devoted to the study of Man, that special being who is of such manifold interest to us all. The principal aim of the first part of the series is to throw light on the two fundamental concepts of knowledge and faith. It discusses the foundations and the limits of human knowledge, and the rôle of faith in relation to science. The second part is devoted to the statement and discussion of all the great truths of salvation which form the contents of divine revelation.

The time has now come to focus our attention on man himself, on his origins, on the two constituent parts of his nature —the body and the soul, in particular on the "dimensions" of that soul, i.e. the portion of the infinite which inheres in it; and finally on those still largely mysterious phenomena which form the subject-matter of the metapsychical sciences.

Any explanation of man must begin with his origins, to which we must now turn our attention. The word *nature* itself, derived from *nasci*, to be born, implies an extremely close relation between man's origins and the deep significance of his place in nature. It must at once be admitted that, if we agree that the evolution of life on this planet culminates in man, so that having achieved its goal its further progress is pursued in and by man alone in what we call history, then we are obviously bound to entertain a singularly lofty and exalted conception of man. Moreover, the very loftiness of this conception will help us to understand the wonderful privileges bestowed on man by divine revelation, and to wonder wholeheartedly at the unique fact of the *Incarnation of a God* by the taking upon himself of human nature in the Person of the Word, the only Son of God.

Furthermore, no study of man's origins can fail to throw light on the very basis of human nature. A formula, which once enjoyed a certain vogue, drew a parallel between the development of the individual and that of the species, asserting that "ontogenesis reproduces phylogenesis". This implied that the human embryo, before reaching maturity, passes once more through all the stages traversed by the species during its evolution towards the human state. Probably no modern scientist would venture to adopt this formula, which nevertheless contains an element, however small, of truth. An understanding of the long process of evolution which culminated in man is undoubtedly of the greatest assistance in understanding human nature.

In this book we shall avail ourselves of any source which may throw light on the mystery of human origins. Even the most dubious evidence is not to be neglected, if only to demonstrate its deficiencies, thereby throwing into greater relief the gift of divine revelation.

We shall, indeed, have much to say concerning the riches contained in this sublime revelation. No one need feel surprised, on opening the Bible, that unique Book containing the charter of our salvation, to find in the very first lines an account, at once poetical and popular, of the creation of the world and of man. St Paul has clearly shown that the temptation and fall of Adam supply the key to the secret of the war waged within each one of us between the flesh and the spirit, and provide one of the main reasons for the mysterious advent of God among men.

Enough has been said to indicate both the magnitude and the difficulties of the subject we are to discuss.

It remains only to indicate briefly the plan we propose to follow.

PLAN OF THIS BOOK

The problems of the origins of man will be investigated along the following main lines:

(1) In the ancient mythologies;

(2) In the ancient and modern philosophers;

(3) In the light of modern scientific discoveries;

(4) In the light of the facts contained in divine revelation and Catholic theology.

The first chapter will describe, of necessity very briefly, how in the total absence of philosophic and scientific knowledge, men indulged their imagination in explaining, by means of more or less improbable "myths", the origin of the human species, the problem of more concern to them than any other.

The second chapter will introduce the earliest philosophies by which men sought an answer to the problem which the myths had failed to solve. Human reason attempts to improve on the guesses of primitive imagination. Here again our treatment of the subject will of necessity be brief and incomplete.

The third chapter will deal with the modern sciences, in particular the comparatively recent science of human palaeontology. It is no longer possible to discuss the origins of man without referring to the evolution of life on our planet.

The fourth chapter will consist of a careful study of the teachings of Catholic theology with regard to human origins. It will discuss the statements to be found in the Scriptures, the interpretation of the principal relevant texts, and the different meanings ascribed from time to time to the accounts given in Genesis.

CHAPTER I

THE ORIGINS OF MAN ACCORDING TO THE MYTHOLOGIES

WHAT IS A MYTH?

There are probably many misinformed readers who may be liable or tempted to confuse a *myth* with a *mystery*. A mystery is a revealed truth, lying beyond the reach of reason though not contradicting it, to which the reason is bound to assent by virtue of the divine authority which reveals it. A myth, on the other hand, is a wholly private creation, ranking among the strangest products of the human mind.

The history of religion begins, at an uncertain but undoubtedly very remote if not earliest date, with a "mythopoetic" age.

The characteristic feature of this period is the desire to tell the story of the origin of things and of man himself.

The word *myth*, which derives from the Greek verb $\mu\hat{v}\theta\epsilon\omega$, "I invent", means a story. A myth is a narrative. It claims to tell the story of the creation of the world by the gods, or of the exploits of the heroes, or of the language of the animals. What we call mythology is a collection of mythical stories.

Myth has its source in the deepest layers of human psychology. In the beginning, man has difficulty in distinguishing between himself and the other beings which surround him, whether they be animals or plants, springs or rocks, or the heavenly bodies. He cannot avoid projecting on to all these things his own feelings and desires. He endows *things*, as we should say today, with a soul resembling his own. He is an unconscious animist. In this way he transforms things, whether they be animate, like the planets and animals, or inanimate like the stars and mountains and rivers, into *persons*. He assigns them a rôle, credits them with purposes and struggles and interventions in his own affairs, and weaves round them a whole history similar to his own. All these stories, sprung from man's imagination, we call myths.

Myth is thus a representation of reality which, though fantastic, claims to be accurate, and commands more or less successfully the belief of the individual. In primitive communities, myth takes the place of science and philosophy. It includes both a religion and a system of ethics. For centuries it has kept alive the faith of mankind in its struggle for the survival of the species against the elements and a hostile nature. Certainly it was not the myth *qua* delusion that benefited the human race, but rather the confidence which it created or preserved.

Wundt has very justly remarked that myth springs from the same source as art; for which reason we said above that religions begin with a "mythopoetic" age. Yet this mythical poetry is not conceived of as poetry in the sense of a pleasant and potent mental pastime. A social group which adopts a myth regards it as a true story requiring to be believed. Its truth consists in the explanation it affords of the institutions and historical traditions of the group. It constitutes for the entire group a spontaneous vision of the universe, of the group's origin and allotted part in the Grand Design, and justifies its existence, its actions and its hopes. More often than not, myth brings into play supernatural forces endowed with an extra-temporal and extra-spatial personality. The most natural and commonplace phenomena such as dawn, lightning, thunder, the motions of the sea in calm or storm, are represented by myth as manifestations of supernatural powers, of a purpose and a will, as portents to be interpreted by the soothsayer's art, as signs of benefits or calamities which it behoves man either to deserve and obtain, or to forestall and avert by the performance of appropriate rites.

USEFULNESS OF MYTH

For a just appreciation of myth, we must consider it in its historical setting. In one sense it may be said that the "truth" of a myth is its "utility".

Now there are three essential points in which myth was of the greatest utility. (1) The myth was the *unifying symbol* of the social group which fashioned it. Within the group, it satisfied the intellectual need to know and to understand, it served as a foundation for religion, it provided the group with a liturgical and moral rule of conduct, and it fostered a community of feeling and of religious sentiment among all the members of the group. A feeling of fraternal union was created round the same stories, the same gods and the same symbols. Thus the myth became the guardian of social discipline. (2) The myth kept alive these same religious sentiments during the numerous and prolonged intervals between bursts of communal enthusiasm when they were in danger of drying up and becoming exhausted. (3) The myth supplied a renewal and reinvigoration of religious faith at the great group demonstrations of loyalty to the gods. At these ceremonies the myth was a mainstay of devotion, imparting to every participant in the religious festivals a powerful sense of community with the group.

For an understanding of the above we may take two fairly simple examples, one deriving from the religion of the patriarchs and transmitted by them first to the Mosaic and then to the Christian religions, the other from the Eleusinian mysteries of the pagan world. When Genesis tells us that the serpent spoke to Eve, that is a "myth": but the Bible itself both explains the myth and reveals all the profound truth contained in it. The "serpent" was simply the devil-tempter, the "Dragon", he who from the beginning was "a liar and a murderer". And a myth of this type may be properly described as one of the most suggestive imaginable, summing up as it does the whole history of mankind. Consequently we may say that the mythical form conceals a truth of the first importance, without which we should be at a great disadvantage in understanding ourselves and in our daily struggle against Satan.

The Greek Eleusinian mysteries set forth the myth of Demeter, goddess of agriculture, seeking for her daughter Kore who was first buried underground and then brought to light once again. This myth was a very obvious symbol of the process of vegetation, whereby the grain first disappears beneath the soil, then makes a triumphant reappearance in the form of a wholly new plant resembling that which originally produced the seed.

But this is not all. A far loftier meaning was contained in this Eleusinian myth—that of human immortality. The Gospel itself was later on to sanction this meaning through the words of Christ: "If the grain of corn dies not, it remains alone, but if it dies it brings forth fruit in abundance." Thus the Eleusinian myth was a wonderful symbol of the destiny of the human soul after the death of the body.

It is true that not all myths are so profound or so easily interpreted; but the two examples given are sufficient to prove that they are not to be lightly regarded or dismissed as inconsistent or ridiculous fables.

VARIETY OF MYTHS

The enormous variety of myths are usually classified in three distinct categories.

(1) *Naturalistic* myths aim at providing an explanation of the principal phenomena—astronomical, meteorological and agricultural—of the natural world. In this first category are to be included the cosmogonical myths which we shall discuss later.

(2) *Historical* myths enable a social group to retain connection with the heroes of its past, for example Rome with Romulus, Egypt with Osiris.

(3) *Explanatory* or *aetiological* myths claim principally to provide the reasons for the rites practised by a social group, for the various shapes assumed by the gods, or for the etymology of words.

But at this point, it becomes of the first importance to note that it is probably as vain to seek for a myth in its pure state as for a pure race. On the contrary, myths must have undergone continuous modification, unrecognized by those concerned. Two kinds of causes must, or may, have been responsible for this circumstance.

In the first place, commercial intercourse, waves of migration, wars and marriages with foreigners, everything in fact that contributed to the mixing of peoples, or of what we have hitherto called "social groups", served also to diffuse legends from one group to another, to bring about a hardly perceptible "contamination" of one myth with another, either by mutual borrowings or by taking over attractive legends or rites credited with some peculiar property. The fact that the Pantheon in Rome kept open house for all the gods shows how minglings of myths and traditions were bound to take place among all the peoples of the world. It is Herodotus who informs us that the Greeks believed they had borrowed much from Egypt. It is indeed impossible to doubt the fact of these borrowings from one people by another. Consequently, for this reason alone, a "pure" myth is something almost inconceivable.

This conclusion is supported by the circumstance that it was the poets, that is to say men endowed with exceptional powers of imagination and invention, who first committed the primitive myths to writing. Is it not unlikely that they refrained from embroidering the legends they reported?

It must be clearly understood that no people, with the exception of the Jews, possessed a *Bible* in the proper meaning of the word, that is to say a collection of sacred and immutable writings. Even in countries where such sacred writings subsequently appeared, they appeared too late to express the primitive indigenous beliefs. The Greeks had forgotten the

Phoenician or Akkadian origin of certain of their gods, the Romans had forgotten the Etruscan origin of certain rites and practices of divination, the Indians had forgotten the Hindu but non-Vedic ancestry of various beliefs. A mixture of primitive myths had taken place long before their final committal to writing. Men were unaware of this blending of gods, but practised unconsciously a kind of syncretism foreshadowing that practised consciously by the more highly developed Greeks and Romans when they installed gods of every origin in their domestic shrines or city temples.

In the words of Fr Pinard de la Boullaye: "For an understanding of Greek mentality we need only observe the striking differences between the genealogies of Homer in the tenth century, of Hesiod in the ninth century, of Pherecydes of Syros, Epimenides of Crete, Acusilaus and the Orphics in the sixth century. The liberties taken by each of these writers with even the most famous of his predecessors imply the existence, not of a prescribed orthodoxy but of a considerable degree of uncertainty."[1]

THEORIES OF THE ORIGINS OF MAN ACCORDING TO PRIMITIVE PEOPLES

The ancient mythologies always framed their views of man's origin within a cosmogony. The problems of the origin of man and of the universe were always envisaged as one and the same problem. And it is above all in this field that the myths proliferated. It follows that the origins of man can be discussed only in relation to the origins of the universe.

We have no knowledge of the primitive cosmogonies. Nevertheless, some idea of them may be formed by studying the beliefs of contemporary backward peoples, who may perhaps preserve their ancient beliefs as they have retained the oldest customs and habits ever practised by mankind.

Let us therefore make a rapid survey of these peoples. The

[1] Pinard de la Boullaye, *L'Etude comparée des religions* (Paris, 1922), I, p. 5.

Pygmies of the great African equatorial forest are commonly considered as the oldest "primitives". They have been carefully studied by visiting missionaries, who have observed with astonishment that, at their artless stage of development, they have retained ideas which are at the same time simple and lofty. Their beliefs seems to be free of the accretions observable in those of peoples with a more advanced economy. This is particularly true of the Pygmies of the Gaboon. According to them the Supreme Being, Kmvum, existed before the beginning of time. He created the world by his sole Word. To this end, he sat down by a stream near the great village of animals, and kneaded statuettes of clay into the shape of a man. He was careful to choose clay of various colours—red, black and white for the diverse races of man. Then he commanded the statuettes to walk, and they obeyed.

According to another myth, in the beginning the Creator was alone in the village. He was bored. There was no one to prepare his meals. Accordingly he resolved to make men. For this purpose he gathered a large number of coconuts, piled them in his canoe by the seashore, and had them towed out to sea by the crocodile. Out in mid-ocean he blew and spat on the nuts, and threw them one by one into the waves, commanding them to turn into men and women.

Similar though vaguer myths may be found in the Belgian Congo among a more important tribe, the Ituri Pygmies. Yet they too worship one God, the Supreme Being called Tore, the creator of both the world and man.

There is also a primitive type of Pygmies in Asia, Negritos of Malacca, or Semangs, natives of the Andaman Islands in the Bay of Bengal. The cosmogonical ideas of the Semangs are vague. They appear to believe in creation by proxy. Two mythical brothers created by the Supreme Being are believed to have made the mountains and hills, from which issued men through the agency of an animal, the dung-beetle, who is said to have created the earth out of the primeval mud.

On the other hand the Andaman Islanders seem to believe in the "auto-creation" of man from a giant bamboo seed. This ancestor was "the solitary one". He had no wife, but lived near an ant-hill by whom he had various children, who were, according to one version, the wind, the storm, the sky and the foam of the sea. Among the southern islanders the notion of a supreme Being is universal. Some call it Puluga, some Biliku, while others say it is a female. This supreme Being is believed to have created the first human pair.

Similar beliefs may be found among peoples considered to be equally primitive, such as the now extinct Tasmanians, the Australians of the boomerang civilization, the African bushmen, the South American Fuegians, etc.

Instead of enumerating a mass of frequently childish details, we prefer here to summarize the features common to these beliefs.

Each of these peoples builds, with individual variations, on an almost identical ground-plan. Recent historico-cultural research, after gathering a rich collection of reliable information, has arrived at the following conclusions.

It is believed that there is a supreme personal Being, creator of all things, and so old that no date can be assigned to his first appearance, nor is any people known to exist which does not recognize him. In the great majority of cases it is this supreme Being who occupies the centre of the cosmogonic myths. He is usually conceived of as possessing human form, but is credited with superhuman attributes. Frequently he creates the universe out of nothing, but more often he creates the earth, the stars, the animals and man out of already existing materials. At this task he either works alone, or employs agents who are beings, even animals, dependent on him and subservient to his orders. Before embarking on his task he usually has before him nothing but chaos, presumably empty space, the sea, the primeval slime, or darkness; and it is from this chaos that he produces the world. The first human beings, consisting either of a single or of several pairs or sometimes of a single male, are made of clay or wood or pliable reeds, etc. The North American Cheyennes say that the first man issued from a rib of the supreme Being; and many tribes agree with our Bible that woman issued from a rib of man (Cheyennes, Nandis of Kenya, Vutis of the Cameroons, Bubis of Fernando Po).

These stories, together with variant versions widely spread among primitive peoples, raise problems difficult to solve owing to the resemblances between the myths and the Bible narrative, since it is not always easy to recognize possible missionary influences, at any rate in the case of Asia and Africa.

Even with peoples among whom the notion of a cosmogony has grown weaker or completely disappeared, it is conceivable that the elements of such a notion did once exist. It may also happen that the primitive myth of the creation of the world and of man is not narrated but symbolically represented in the initiation rites of puberty. This is the case with the Central Australians, some Cheyenne tribes, and many others. This circumstance is of great significance as proving that beliefs concerning the creation of the world and of man were regarded as the basis of the customs of the social group in question.

THEORIES OF THE ORIGINS OF MAN ACCORDING TO SECONDARY CIVILIZATIONS

Passing from "primitive" to "secondary" civilizations, that is, to further advanced peoples already practising agriculture and various rudimentary industries, we find more complex stories which admit, side by side with the universally recognized supreme God, a polytheistic and sometimes extremely complicated mythology. Moreover, it seems as if mythical elements have been diffused from higher cultures to geographically far distant regions.

This is most apparent in Polynesia. The American ethnologist Stimson has recently translated the following powerfully inspired Polynesian hymn:

"O Thou, God, who dwellest in heaven!
O Thou, the unnameable only One!

O Thou, God, whose manifestations are without number!
O Thou, God, creator of all things. . . .
Incline thy mercy towards us,
For thou art the gracious God,
Thou art the bountiful God.
O Thou, the unnameable only One,
Holy, holy art thou!"

As an example of a widely diffused cosmogonical story we may take the "cosmic egg" myth, which is found in Indian as well as Polynesian civilizations. From this egg the world and man in particular are said to have been hatched. The same story is found among the Yorubas of British Nigeria in West Africa, a people in an advanced stage of agriculture. Nevertheless, an Asiatic influence cannot always be assumed, for the stories, after beginning with the "cosmic egg", often present wide divergencies.

For example, the Australian Bad tribe have an egg which produces the flood and the rainbow, while another Australian tribe, the Wimmera, have the egg of an emu, a large bird which is a cross between the nandu and the cassowary, from which are hatched the sun, and from the sun mankind.

In Polynesia the following is an example of a cosmogony belonging to a people in the secondary stage of civilization. A sky-god (Tangaloa in Samoa as in Tonga, and Tangaroa in New Zealand) is imagined in the shape of a bird. He has the sun for an eye, and a huge rock for wife called O-te-papa, and on this wife he begets other gods and stars, together with the sea and the winds. He also produces the first men, whom he fashions out of red earth.

According to other myths, the "maker of the sky" was a son of Tangaroa called Raitubu. In Mangaia, in the Cook Islands, it is believed that a powerful but invisible agent caused the world in which we live to issue from an original chaos composed of mud. According to an alternative version, the "Great Mother" (Vari-ma-te-takere, from a word which also means mud) made all the gods and living creatures out of fragments of her own substance. Thus everything comes from the earth, which was itself not created but extracted from darkness or the night.

The Maoris of New Zealand believe that in the beginning there was the sky and the earth (Rangi and Papa), and that they clung together in the primal darkness, in whose depths there was already living a primitive human pair.

It was a son of Rangi and Papa called Tanemahuta, a name meaning "father of the forests", who, after consulting his brothers the gods, determined to revolt against his parents. He placed his head against the "earth-mother" and his feet against the "sky-father", and tore them apart despite their cries of pain. This was the origin of light and of the cosmic order as it now exists.

Similar conceptions are to be met with a long way from New Zealand among the Upper Guinea tribes of Achantis, Edos, Yorubas and Ibibios.

It is always from the original pair sky-earth that the world is born, together with a multitude of lesser gods who have charge of the firmament, the thunder, the sea, etc., and are always at war with each other and with their parents the sky and the earth. Often we find the idea that men were begotten by the gods, a belief which we shall see recurring in many cosmogonies. It may be remembered that such an intelligent man as Julius Caesar believed in his descent through Aeneas from the goddess Venus.

Among certain peoples of the Upper Niger such as the Bambaras, the Dogons, the Bozos, etc., we find metaphysical ideas concealed beneath a mythical form. According to the Dogons' cosmogony it was Amma, the one omnipotent God, who created the stars by hurling lumps of earth into space. The sun was of white-hot earthenware bound in copper, and the moon was fashioned in similar style. The earth was created by Amma, and was imagined as a woman impregnated by Water, which is a seed of the gods. From Earth and Water sprang two twin jinn, sharers of the divine nature and endowed with the gift of speech, who partook of the divine power inherent in Water. This original and perfectly united pair of jinn spoke to the earth, thereby imparting to it the Word which is the vehicle of power and begetter of all things. They traced on the ground the male and female souls, and beneath the "shadows" of these patterns there lay down together the first man and the first woman, fashioned of clay by God separately from Earth and flung down from the heights of heaven.

This brief sketch may suffice to give some idea of the theories entertained by the "secondary" civilizations regarding the origins of man.

We must now turn to the so-called higher civilizations: the Ancient East—India and China, Mexico and Peru, the Greco-Roman world; and the western world of such peoples as the Celts and Teutons.

We shall endeavour to follow a chronological plan, beginning with the oldest civilizations, or those at least with which we have been longest acquainted.

EGYPT

The dominant theology of ancient Egypt was that which took shape in Heliopolis, not far from modern Cairo. It is calculated that the doctrines taught in this centre go back more than thirty centuries to between 3000 and 4000 B.C. They are known to us from fully authenticated documents, the fifth-century pyramid texts.

Heliopolis was one of the oldest cities in Egypt, and even after the foundation of Memphis and Thebes, remained the capital city. It was also an intellectual centre, for Egyptian religion, like Druidism, embraced all the then known sciences. The university of Heliopolis, all traces of which have disappeared, survived up to the Roman period.

We must now examine the cosmogony taught in this ancient sanctuary. In the beginning, according to this doctrine, was the primordial water, the mysterious ocean of chaos, called Nu or Nun. Here dwell Atum, also called Tum, the first god. He it was who fashioned the world. There was as yet neither sky nor earth, nor plants nor animals. So Atum issued from chaos in the shape of a sun, and since the sun is called Ra in Egyptian, he was called Atum-Ra or Ra-Atum, or finally simply Ra. By day he was Ra, and by night Atum. In the morning he was also called Ra-Khopri, or Ra the Beetle, to indicate that he lives and is re-born from himself, for the Egyptians like other peoples already mentioned always looked on the beetle as the symbol of rebirth and resurrection. Care was taken to insert a beetle near the heart of every mummy, as a guarantee of return to a new life. In pictures and underground murals and funerary papyri, when the sun sails on the waters of the river of night and is about to reappear on the horizon, he is depicted in his boat with the body of a man but the head of a beetle. By day, as he mounts the sky, Ra is depicted with the same body, but with the head of a falcon crowned with the solar disk and the uraeus or serpent-emblem. In his rôle of Atum, or first Principle, his head is always that of a man.

It is clear from the above that Atum, though issuing from chaos, did not create it. It follows that the notion of a creation *ex nihilo* was foreign to the Egyptians. As we shall see, this notion in its pure state will not be found until we come to the Hebrews: no ancient people entertained it with sufficient clarity.

Nevertheless the Egyptians invoked their God Atum-Ra or Amon-Ra in the following terms which remind us of the Polynesian prayer quoted above:

"O Thou who madest all the gods together with all men and things." But their conception of this creation seems to be rather that of an organizing process starting from the pre-existent chaos or Nu.

The doctrine of Heliopolis describes this process in symbolic and mysterious terms. The first god Atum-Ra, who draws his life from himself, is also self-fertilizing. He has eight offspring, four male and four female, coupled in pairs in the following order: Shu and Tafnut, Qeb or Seb and Nut, Osiris and Isis, Set and Nephthys. But the latter two couples are only the grandchildren of Atum-Ra, since they are the children of the second couple Qeb and Nut. We have therefore nine gods including Atum. The number, however, is not fixed. Sometimes we have ten, eleven or twelve, the rôles being subdivided.

As we have seen, the first couple consists of Shu and Tafnut. Shu is a god with human form, known as the eldest son of Ra. In the creation of the world his function is to slip between Qeb and Nut, to separate them, to lift up Nut (symbol of the sky) by the waist, and to hold her aloft bent like an arch, so that, to the east by her toes and to the west by her fingers she remains in touch with Qeb, symbol of the earth. Poised thus, Shu is evidently the atmosphere supporting the firmament. In his numerous surviving statues he is represented kneeling on one knee with both hands raised to the level of the head as if lifting a weight.

Tafnut, the sister of Shu, is a shadowy figure. The second couple, Qeb and Nut, are of much greater importance. Qeb is the earth, and Nut is the sky. After being separated by Shu they became the progenitors of all subsequent creatures. Qeb, like Adam in the Bible, is the first father; Nut, the first mother, symbolizes the firmament.

Osiris and Isis, the first-born children of Qeb and Nut, are the two most famous gods of Egypt. Later on, Osiris seems to have become the symbol of the first man, and Isis of the first woman.[1]

BABYLONIA

Babylonian, like Egyptian theories of the origin of man, cannot be studied apart from their accompanying cosmogony. Babylonian cosmogony is familiar to us principally from the great epic poem *Enuma elis*, which relates the contest of the god Bel or Marduk with the monster Tiamat. This poem survives in a seventh-century B.C. Assyrian version, but it undoubtedly dates from very much earlier. It consists of seven

[1] For a full account of ancient Egyptian religion see the volume of this series devoted to the subject.

tablets, each containing about 140 lines. Of these we possess a large portion, but the final three tablets are so mutilated as to present considerable gaps.

A careful summary must now be given of this cosmogony, since it has often been compared with that of Genesis, to which, however, it is greatly inferior in sublimity and beauty.

There was in the beginning, according to the Babylonian poem, a watery chaos represented by a triad consisting of Apsu-Tiamat-Mummu. Apsu is the ocean, Tiamat the sea. They mingle their waters, and personify chaos. It is they who beget the gods. Thus we see that the cosmogony begins with a theogony. The gods represent order emerging from chaos. The third couple to spring from this chaos consists of Anshar and Kishar, who represent the upper and the lower parts of the as yet unformed firmament. But additional gods are born, and Apsu complains that their activity disturbs his rest: "By day I have no rest, at night I cannot sleep!"

He therefore consults Tiamat, and together they determine to destroy the gods. The god Ea frustrates this plan. Tiamat, in a rage, brings forth serpents and dragons and monsters of every description, and launches them against the gods. The god Anu is sent to give battle, but the mere sight of Tiamat so terrifies the coward that he takes to flight. Finally the god Marduk, the future Bel, the patron god of Babylon, agrees to give battle on condition of being promoted above all the gods. The condition is accepted at a banquet at which everyone gets drunk. Marduk arms himself for the fray. "He sets a flash of lightning on his face, he fills his whole body with a burning flame, he makes a net to ensnare Tiamat, he takes the four winds so that nothing of her may escape him—the south wind, the north wind, the east wind, the west wind—and gathers them beside the net, a present from his father Anu."

Borne on a whirlwind, Marduk advances upon Tiamat. The monster opens her jaws to devour him. He hurls in a storm-blast, and pierces her body with an arrow. With one half of the body he covers the sky, and to prevent the waters on high from falling, he fits a bolt and appoints a watchman, thereby constituting the firmament of the upper waters. He then installs in the sky the stars, the planets, the moon and the sun. Lastly, with the other half of Tiamat's body, he constructs the earth, which covers the subterranean world. From the surviving fragments of the concluding tablets, with the help of Berosius, it seems that Marduk fashions mankind out of blood, perhaps from his own blood. The obvious purpose of this poem is to elevate Marduk, the god of Babylon, above all the gods, thereby creating a kind of universal hegemony for the benefit of Babylon.

It is impossible to deny to some parts of this poem a certain grandeur deriving from its theme of the creation of the universe. At the same time we cannot fail to note that it attributes to the deity a number of feelings and actions irreconcilable with the dignity of the supreme Being.

PERSIA

Persian theories of the origins of man present a novel feature which may be called the problem of evil. It is true that this problem was not unknown to other cosmogonies. The Indians of Central California and the Algonquins show unmistakable traces of a "Prince of Evil". In California he is identified with the coyote, the prairie wolf. But he does not come on the scene until after the supreme Being has finished or almost finished his work of creation. In Siberia this prince of evil is known as Erlik, and elsewhere as Ngaa or Shaitan.

But it is Persia that offers the clearest account of the conflict between good and evil: this it does by the doctrine of *dualism*, in other words the *duality of the first Principles*.

The two most important Persian treatises on the creation are the Vendidad and the Bundahishn, at which we will now glance.

Before the creation, there existed infinite time, *Zervan akarana*. With the creation there commences a first period of 12,000 years. During the first 3,000 years Ahura Mazda, the principle of light (identical with Ormazd or Ormuzd), maintains the universe in an immaterial state, by which is meant that nothing existed except the *fravāshis* or *spirits* of things, roughly equivalent to the Latin "genii", the Greek "daemons", or the Christian guardian angels. But at this point Anro-Mainyar—or Ahriman, to use his shorter name, the principle of evil, awakes from his state of torpor. Mazda offers to make peace: Ahriman refuses. A 9,000 years' war breaks out between the two. Mazda strikes Ahriman with an all-powerful prayer, the *Ahuna Vairya*, and stuns him. The 3,000 years succeeding the outbreak of war witness the creation of the material beings whose prototypes or *fravāshis* are already in existence: the sky, the water, the earth, the plants, the animals *and man*. During the next 3,000 years Ahriman (Anro-Mainyar) strives desperately to deface the whole of creation. He slays the primordial bull. He slays the first man (*Gayo maretan*). From their bodies there come forth respectively animals and men. The most famous of the old-time kings was Yima, whose reign of a thousand years was a golden age which ended in collapse, whereupon he was dethroned by the dragon Azhi Dahaka. Yima corresponds to the Hindu Yama who, according to the Veda, was *the first man*, the first to die and the king of the blessed, but who in brahminic India became the god of the infernal regions.

Finally, the last 3,000 years' period opens with the revelation made to Zarathustra or Zoroaster, and the conversion of King Vishtaspa. This new age was to be noted for the appearance of a series of prophets (*saoshyant*) culminating in the appearance of Astvatereta, the prophet *par excellence*. Competent scholars have suggested that the Magi who came to Bethlehem were acquainted with this prophecy. At the end of the 12,000 years, that is about the year 2000 A.D., will come the general resurrection, preceded by the end of this present world. This will mark the victory of Mazda, the principle of light, over his adversary the principle of darkness, and the beginning of a new age which will last for ever.

It is impossible to deny that this picture attains to a true sublimity.

HINDU COSMOGONIES

Passing from Persia to India we are confronted by not one but many cosmogonies, since the accounts given in the sacred books of India are not always the same. A famous hymn in the Rig-Veda contains the following lines:

"There was no non-being, there was no being; there was neither atmosphere nor the sky above. What was it that moved? Where? Under whose protection? What was the water of the deep, unfathomable sea? ... Without producing any wind, self-activated, the One (*Tad equam*) breathed, and outside him there was nothing. ... Whence came the creation and who produced it, whether he or not he who is the supreme guardian in heaven of this world, he alone knows for certain, unless indeed he knows nothing about it" (Rig-Veda 10, 129).

In Rig-Veda 10, 81 and 82, the creation of the world is attributed to Vishvakarman, and in 10, 121 to Prajāpati. Elsewhere Prajāpati is identified with Vishvakarma the creator. In Brahmanism it is usually Prajāpati who produces the universe from his own substance, and by the practice of ascetic exercises gives birth to the earth, the atmosphere and the sky. But all the texts betray the priestly presumption according to which the origin of the universe results from the magic action of religious ceremonies. Finally, towards the seventh century B.C. the Vedas and the Brahmanas underwent a metaphysical interpretation. At this point philosophy may be said to take over from mythology. We shall return to this subject in the next chapter.

In the Upanishads everything proceeds from Brahma, the self-existent absolute being who creates the gods and assigns to them the government of the world.

Jainism (sixth century B.C.) and Buddhism are best regarded as species of philosophy.[1]

---

[1] Brahmanism and Buddhism, Confucianism, Taoism and Shintoism are more fully discussed in two further volumes of this series.

CHINESE COSMOGONY

The ancient Chinese religion seems not to have included any cosmogony properly so called, and appears to contain no cosmological myth. Nevertheless, a comparison of various legends with analogous Indo-Chinese myths has led Maspero to suggest that China, like other countries, once had traditions such as the following concerning the creation:

The earth was covered by the waters. After its emergence it was peopled by one of the sons of the Lord of Heaven, who was sent down expressly for the purpose. Thus the sky and the earth, who are the greatest of the gods, explain all that follows.

We shall have occasion in the next chapter to refer to Confucianism and Taoism, as well as to the monistic-materialist theory of the first-century A.D. Wang Ch'ung. This, however, belongs properly to philosophy.

MEXICO AND PERU

In pre-Columbian America two cosmogonical myths deserve mention, one from the Mayas of Mexico, the other from Peru. The Mayas, who then as now occupied Central America, were a highly civilized people. According to their cosmogony, in the beginning the sky and the water were stagnant and shrouded in darkness. Gucumatz, Tepeu and Hurrakan took counsel and created the world, consisting of mountains, plains and rivers. Next appeared the vegetable followed by the animal kingdoms. Lastly, the gods made man out of chalk. But a drawback quickly showed itself: man began to dissolve in the water. The gods then called on Xpicacoc and Xumcam to help make a man from the wood of one tree, and a woman from the bark of another: these, however, had no mind. It was not until after a flood that four intelligent and perfect men were created. They were gifted with both long and near sight. Moved by jealousy, the earlier race of men struck the newcomers in the eyes, so that thenceforward they could only see near to. While all four slept, the gods created four women, thus making possible the propagation of the human race.

According to the Peruvians it was Con, offspring of the sun and moon, who created both the world and man. Con was displeased with the people of the coast, and changed their land into desert. But after a time he agreed to create rivers and pastures and fruits to provide sustenance for man. At this point Con was replaced by Pachamac, another child of the sun and moon, who transformed into animals the men created by his brother. But he made other men, the Indians of historical times who practised agriculture and horticulture.

THE GRECO-ROMAN WORLD

The Greeks and the Romans are here dealt with together for the reason that the latter, whose worship was originally directed towards chthonic gods of the humblest and earthiest nature, ended by adopting and adapting the Greek myths. These myths had themselves been subjected to frequent rehandling. The most coherent account of them is generally considered to be that contained in the poems of Hesiod, whose real object was to construct a theogony, or genealogy of the gods, which should at the same time be both a cosmogony and an account of the origins of man.

Before Hesiod, Homer contributes the following: Earth is surrounded by a great stream called Ocean, which is the humid element in general, imagined as a constantly moving ring encircling the earth. Homer states definitely that "all things were born of Ocean" (*Iliad* 14, 246), although a few lines above in the same book of the *Iliad* (14, 201) he says that Ocean was the father and Thetis the mother of all things. Thetis is thought to symbolize "the foster-mother", that is, the Earth. With these two is often associated the goddess Night.

According to Alfred Croiset the poems of Hesiod were composed round about 800 B.C. Their aim is to attempt a synthesis of the legends about the gods. There were in the beginning four beings: Chaos (which we find undoubtedly recurring in nearly all the ancient cosmogonies, particularly in the East), the Earth or Gaia, Tartarus in the depths of the earth, and Eros or Love. Here Chaos probably means empty space. From Chaos sprang Erebus (Darkness) and Nyx (Night). From Nyx and Erebos sprang Hemera (Day) and Aither (Upper Air or Sky). Gaia in her turn produced Uranos (the sky), the mountains and Pontos (the sea). The mating of Gaia and Uranos produced a multitude of gods, the Titans, the Cyclopes, the hundred-handed Giants. But revolution soon broke out: Uranos, for his cruel treatment of his children, was deposed by Kronos. And now there appear on the scene the Fates and Death and Sleep and Dreams and Old Age, all conceived of as divine beings. A place is also found in this richest of all mythologies for the charming Nymphs and for the horrible or menacing Harpies, the Chimeras, the Gorgons and the Sphinx. Meanwhile Zeus has deposed his father Kronos. The Titans then revolt against Zeus, who with the help of the hundred-handed Giants succeeds in hurling them into Tartarus. A final victory over the monster Typhon established Zeus securely on the throne. The stage is now set for the entrance of the Olympian gods.

Like Greek theology, the poems of Hesiod became a repository often consulted and freely interpreted.

Thus there were many versions of this ancient theogony, and the imagination of the poets revelled in the unending invention of myths. In this connection account must be taken of the interests of the various cities or tribes. Each one of these boasted its own particular god, whom it regarded as its special patron, and from whom it never wearied of demanding protection for crops and herds, promotion of fertility in women and prosperity in trade and commerce, regardless of whether such functions were included in the traditional attributes of the local divinity. On the other hand, numerous contaminations crept into the traditions through contact with neighbouring peoples, particularly those of the East.

THE MYTH OF PROMETHEUS

It is of particular interest to trace, by means of a striking example, the way in which a theory of the origin of man is linked with a cosmogony. Throughout this chapter we have seen that the former is inseparable from the latter, of which it is merely a part, an episode. This is well illustrated by the myth of Prometheus.

According to the Greco-Roman tradition, Prometheus was not a man but the God or Spirit of Fire. And it was Prometheus who created man. He was the personification of the creative and inventive genius. With the help of Athena, goddess of wisdom and intelligence, he had fashioned man out of clay. He had then brought man to life by stealing a spark of the heavenly fire. This first man was called Deucalion. According to other legends, Deucalion was merely the son of Prometheus and Pandora. But the creation of man contravened the will of Zeus, who had become king of the gods through his victory over the Titans. Zeus sent the flood to destroy mankind. But Prometheus saved Deucalion by teaching him to build a ship, shaped like an enormous chest, which floated for nine days and finally came to rest on a lofty mountain. Deucalion's wife Pyrrha had also been saved from the flood. This Pyrrha, according to the legend, was the daughter of Pandora and Epimetheus. However that may be, it was Deucalion and Pyrrha who, after the flood, produced the entire race of mankind. They were instructed what to do by an oracle. All that was required was to throw behind them "the bones of their mother". Being the children of Earth they understood perfectly that these "bones" were stones. Accordingly they threw behind them some stones—bones of the earth, the mother of mankind—and each stone thrown by Deucalion became a man, while each thrown by Pyrrha became a woman. According to the legend, all this took place in Thessaly. But there were numerous variant traditions, according to some of which Deucalion landed on Etna or on Mount Athos. He was said to have been born at Dodona or at Delphi, both seats of famous Hellenic oracles. His tomb was pointed out both at Delphi and Athens. But through his son Hellen, the father of Aeolus, he was accounted ancestor of all the Greeks.

As for Prometheus, he had been punished by Zeus for three causes of offence: cheating Zeus in a sacrifice, creating the first man, and stealing the heavenly fire, the secret of all life. For his punishment, Zeus had had him chained by Hephaistos to a rock in the Caucasus, where an eagle continued to gnaw his liver, which continued to grow again. He was, however, finally pardoned, for helping Zeus by giving warning of a plot to overthrow him.

This myth of Prometheus is undoubtedly one of the most suggestive in the whole of Greek antiquity.

CELTIC COSMOGONY AND THEORIES OF THE ORIGINS OF MAN

Any attempt to reconstruct primitive Celtic cosmogony and theory of the origins of man presents great difficulties. This is due to the fact that Julius Caesar in his account of the religion of the Gauls persisted, possibly with a view to political fusion, in substituting Latin for Gallic gods, thus making it difficult for us to determine the names, origins and functions of the ancient Celtic gods.

Nevertheless, the theogony and cosmogony of the Celts seems to have been in no way inferior in profusion of legends and symbolic myths to those of the Greeks, to whom the Celts were far closer than to the Romans, that tough and practical but unimaginative people.

The Celtic legends have probably survived in part among the Irish and the island Celts. But the writers who recorded them had been Christians for centuries, and have themselves toned down and edited many of the tales they reported, while constantly insisting that they did not believe one word of them.

With regard to the origins of man, it is perhaps possible to distinguish one doctrine common to all branches of the Indo-

European family of peoples, namely the belief that the gods were the ancestors rather than the creators of mankind. The Gauls, according to Caesar, claimed descent from a god. Caesar calls him Dis Pater, but that is a Latin name. The god in question might be the Irish Dagde or Dago-Devos, the good god, also known as Eochu, Ollathair, the universal father.

Like the Gauls, the Irish certainly claimed a divine origin. Many of their gods occupy a pre-eminent place in the ancient genealogies of their kings. Noteworthy among these gods is Nuadu-Lugh, the god of light who gave his name to Lyons (Lugdunum), Manannan mac Lir the son of the sea, known also as Oirbsiu Mor. The old genealogists placed his dwelling under the waters of Lough Corrib. And in fact the lake bears his name—Lough Oirbsen—and in times of drought the local inhabitants believe they can see the chimneys of his house at the bottom of the lake.

GERMANIC COSMOGONY AND THEORIES OF THE ORIGINS OF MAN

The same considerations apply to the Germanic as to the Irish legendary tales. As a result of Christian editing they reveal features borrowed from Christianity. After removal of later accretions, they may be summarized as follows.

In the beginning was the void, the equivalent of the chaos which we have encountered so often. In the north there took shape the land of cold, Niflheim, and in the south the realm of fire, Muspellsheim. Between the two lay a vast chasm called Ginnungagap. From Niflheim a multitude of streams flowed down into the chasm, where the water became frozen. But from Muspellsheim showers of sparks flew out and melted the ice. Thus were born Ymir, father of the heavenly giants, and the cow Audhumla, his wet-nurse. The cow subsisted by licking the frozen salty stones. On the evening of the first day on which she had licked these stones there appeared a man's hair, followed on the second day by his head, and on the third day by the whole man. His name was Buri, and he was the father of Bor, who begat Odin, Vili and Vei. These three slew Ymir, and out of his dead body created the earth, the sea and the firmament. The legend described in detail how each of Ymir's members was used in the making of the earth, the mountains, the rocks, the trees, the sea, the clouds, etc. Odin and his two brothers found on the shore two trees, from which they fashioned the first human pair, Askr and Embla.

The experts are agreed that in all this there are to be found inventions of the Scaldic, i.e. Scandinavian, poets of a late period; it is, however, impossible to determine how much genuinely primitive material is embedded in the stories as we have them.

Enough has now been said in this chapter to demonstrate that throughout history men have taken an interest in the origins of themselves and of the world. It is also clear that at all times they have attributed the origin of mankind and the universe to superior supernatural beings, different from the familiar dwellers on this earth. Very few cosmogonies have ventured to say whether the world was made out of nothingness or from pre-existing material. Most often we hear of chaos. But chaos is not necessarily an everlasting substance. The word may have indicated merely "the void", and served to translate the abstract idea of "nothingness".

In the next chapter we shall see how the philosophers claimed to correct these mythical notions, and to replace them by rational and metaphysical theories.

CHAPTER II

PHILOSOPHY AND THE PROBLEM OF ORIGINS

PHILOSOPHIES AND MYTHS

Not everything in the mythologies was futile and childish: far from it. They may have provided puerile solutions for the great human problems, but at any rate they did pose these very problems: whence comes the world, and whence comes man, and what is his place and rôle in nature? What is the origin of evil? Such problems, as we have seen, lay at the bottom of the inventions of the mythologies. And since the most rudimentary civilizations provided the barest, simplest and loftiest answers to these problems, we are justified in supposing that from time immemorial men have entertained thoughts, or rather beliefs, of the same kind as we find among the modern Pygmies and Negritos of Africa and Asia.

But a time came when the hitherto accepted answers to such problems seemed "laughable" to a few more enlightened thinkers. By the time of the Persian wars we find Hecataeus of Miletus writing of the myths and legends of the peoples with whom he was acquainted: "I set down these things according as they seem to me true, for the stories told by the Greeks are inconsistent, and many of them are in my opinion absurd."

Such a remark indicates that the task of explanation had been taken over from the poets by a new type of mind. The mythopoetic age was over, the age of the philosophers had begun.

We are here faced with a revolution in human thought, the precise nature of which requires definition. As with most revolutions—for example our own industrial revolution—the birth of this one passed almost unnoticed. It affected only a few minds, nor would it ever command such a large audience as mythology. While the ignorant and superstitious mob continued to feed on the ancient myths and legends, an imperceptible élite gradually grew up, devoted to the quest for more solid, more rational and human solutions of the problems posed. To begin with, this élite gathered few disciples. But in the long run the myths were dethroned and reduced to their present-day status of "fairy tales".

Yet it remains true that this goal would never have been reached by pure philosophy without the powerful inspiration of the Christian revelation.

PRE-LOGICAL MENTALITY

Are we therefore, as some have thought, to attribute to our remote ancestors who invented the myths a mentality differing *in toto* from our own? The French philosopher Lucien Lévy-Bruhl (1857–1939) became widely known for his theories on this subject. In various works, such as *Les Fonctions mentales dans les sociétés inférieures* (1910) and *La Mentalitê primitive* (1922), he applied the adjective "pre-logical" to the type of thinking revealed in the mythologies. At the same time, in an important lecture delivered at Oxford in 1931 he conceded that the mystical forms in which primitives expressed themselves did not prevent them from possessing those elements of rationality which are to be found in every human intelligence. "In all men," says Jacques Chevalier, "whether primitive or civilized, reason is governed by the same principles that constitute the rationality of nature: it postulates order, and it insists that there is no such thing as chance, that everything has a purpose, and that everything is linked to a cause or a reason which determines its existence and value, even when such cause or reason eludes or outstrips our understanding."[1]

It follows that the primitive is not ignorant of the principle

[1] J. Chevalier, *Histoire de la Pensée*, I, p. 24.

of causality. He applies its rules in his daily activities. But in his search for causes he allows his imagination to invent phantasies which open the door to magical interventions and superstitious hopes.

The function of philosophy is precisely to come to closer grips with the problems, to start again from the beginning in the search for causes, and to reach if possible definite conclusions. Wisdom, according to a famous saying, is "knowledge of causes".

THE BIRTH OF PHILOSOPHY

We have remarked that the philosophical revolution was the work of an imperceptible élite. But not every people produced such an élite. Even civilizations of the greatest brilliance, such as Babylonia or Egypt, failed to attain to philosophy, and became enmeshed in magic or divination. As we shall see, neither Hindu nor Chinese thinkers succeeded in emerging into a rational philosophy properly so called. Only Greece gave birth to a line of thinkers who won for themselves first the name of "sages", and then the more modest title of "philosophers"—"lovers of wisdom".

How did the Greeks acquire this privilege? Many explanations have been proposed. In the first place it is obvious that the life of the dweller in woods or caves did not lend itself to the birth of philosophy. But as soon as a sedentary replaced of wealth in a few hands, it became possible for an élite to a nomadic life, involving division of labour and concentration devote its leisure to reflection and to the disinterested pursuit of learning. Yet this explanation is not enough, for not every people can show the same results from the enjoyment of wealth and leisure. For an explanation of what has been called "the miracle of Greece" we are driven to fall back on the mystery of race.

We must avoid the error of speaking of "pure race". On the contrary, the Hellenic race was probably the product of a fusion of Aegean, Minoan and Mycenean peoples with

Achaean invaders who arrived from Central Europe at the close of the Bronze Age. This mixture produced an astonishingly gifted people, at once intelligent and inquisitive, rational and intuitive, artistic and practical, and appreciative of the formal principles inherent in nature, the arts and the law. It was a people enjoying perpetual youth, as was remarked by the Egyptian priest mentioned by Plato in the Timaeus: "You Greeks never grow up; you are always children at heart."

Wherever they went the Greeks retained this gift of perpetual youth. They delighted in making all nature their playground. Moreover, since Greece possessed flourishing colonies, and maintained widespread commercial relations with both east and west, her seafaring sons enjoyed sources of information, comparison and intercourse which few other peoples could command.[1]

THE SAGES AND THE ORIGINS OF MAN

Confronted with the mythical accounts of the past, the earliest Greek sages might quite simply have turned aside and confined themselves to the empirical sciences such as geography, history, physics, mathematics, etc. It is all the more remarkable that they in their turn were attracted by the great problems posed in the mythologies. They were anxious to discover what the world was made of and who made it and reduced it to order. For them, as for their forebears, cosmogony included the origins of man; like ourselves they made no attempt to separate the second from the first. On this particular point there is no difference between the procedures of science or Christian theology and those of philosophy and mythology.

Bearing this in mind, let us now attempt to indicate the distinguishing features of the earliest Greek thinkers.

[1] See J. Chevalier, op. cit., I, pp. 63ff. See also, by the same author, the volume in this series on the origin of Christian philosophy.

DIFFERENCES OF APPROACH

How did the philosophers envisage the problem of man's origins? They reveal wide differences of approach.

The earliest Greek sages applied themselves to the collection of myths and to the description of such religious practices as they had been able to observe in the course of their travels. We have already quoted Hecataeus of Miletus as evidence for the birth of a critical spirit regarding the myths. This does not mean that in the sixth century enquiring minds like Hecataeus, or in the fifth century men like Charon of Lampsacus, Xanthus of Lydia, Hellanicus of Lesbos, Herodotus "the Father of History", and a little later Ctesias of Cnidus, freed themselves at one stroke from the old mythologies. On the contrary, the trouble they took in recording them, while condemning certain details as "ridiculous", proves that they accepted their general meaning while reserving freedom of interpretation.

These men are scholars rather than philosophers. The great names in the beginning of philosophy are those of Thales of Miletus (c. 640–546), his contemporary Anaximander of Miletus, Anaximenes of Miletus (died c. 528) and lastly Heraclitus (c. 576–480). Our knowledge of their philosophy is too fragmentary and imperfect to afford any clear idea of their views on the origins of man. Each in his own way formulated a cosmogony, but it is impossible to say what place was occupied by the origins of man in their explanations of the universe, whose primary material was variously asserted to be water, or "the boundless", or air, or fire.

PYTHAGORAS AND THE MYSTICISM OF NUMBERS

The first problem to engage the attention of the thinkers mentioned above was that of the material origin of the world. What seems most to have interested them was the stuff of which the world, and consequently man, was made. With

Pythagoras we pass from the *material* to the *formal* cause of all things, and particularly of man.

Pythagoras wrote nothing. His teaching, summarized by his disciples in the "Golden Verses", constitutes less a cosmogony than an ethics of the loftiest character.

But this ethical system itself implies, even if unconsciously, a theory of the origins of man. We saw in the preceding chapter that the mythologies nearly always established a family relationship between man and the divine, sometimes going so far as to make man the son of a god. Pythagoras adopted this fine idea, transformed it and purified it. In the "Golden Verse" we find the following: "Meditate, love and live those things which will set your feet on the way of the divine nature. *The race of men is divine, and holy nature reveals to them the most hidden mysteries.*"

In reading these words it is impossible not to be reminded of the saying of the poet quoted by St Paul before the Areopagus: "For indeed we too are of His race" (Acts 17. 28).

Thus the Pythagorean theory of the origin of man comes very close to the Christian faith: and from the theory Pythagoras drew the most splendid consequences. According to him all men are brothers and friends, *because they are of the race of God*. This Pythagorean formula was constantly quoted by the ancients and evidently inspired the poet Aratus quoted by St Paul.

Aristotle in the *Metaphysics* says: "Those who are called Pythagoreans were the first to devote themselves to mathematics, in which they made advances. They were led by their investigations to consider mathematical principles *as the principles of all things*. Since, of these principles, numbers are by nature the first, and seeing that the Pythagoreans thought they could perceive in numbers a better analogy to what is, or is coming into being in the world, than can be found in Fire or Earth or Water—one arrangement of numbers constituting justice, another the soul and the intellect, another opportunity, and similarly to a certain extent with all the other arrangements; and seeing, furthermore, that they recognized that the properties and relations of musical harmonies correspond to numerical ratios; and since, finally, everything in the whole of nature seemed to them to be formed in the likeness of numbers, in so far as numbers are the primordial realities of the universe, they arrived at the conviction that the elements of numbers are the elements of everything that exists, and that the whole heavens are composed of harmony and number. And they brought together all the correspondences they could discover between numbers and musical harmonies and the phenomena of the firmament and its parts and the order of the universe, and combined them into one coherent system."

Pythagoras, then, created a veritable mysticism of numbers, traces of which can easily be found in St Augustine when, for example, he explains why the number 153, which is the number of the fish caught in the miraculous draught described in the Gospel of St John, after the resurrection, is a number which clearly signifies the elect and the blessed in heaven.

Be that as it may, it is the great glory of Pythagoras to have discovered that nature was harmoniously created, that everything good is harmony and order, that everything can be expressed in numbers. The exaggeration with which his teaching can be charged consists in his having made numbers not merely a means of expression of the universal harmony, but the principle and cause of that harmony itself.

THE ATOMISTIC THEORY

Plato and Aristotle will provide a profounder explanation of the order governing the cosmos and the origins of man, who is the coping-stone of the cosmos. But before dealing with them, we must first examine the attempt at a mechanistic explanation of the universe made by Democritus and the Atomists.

The Eleatic school had reduced everything to Oneness; Heraclitus conceived of everything as in motion. Democritus and the Atomists attempted to reconcile the unchangeable One with the fact of movement. The atom of Democritus is "of necessity one and unchangeable". It has been reserved to our own times to witness the "splitting of the atom". Ever since Democritus the atom has been regarded as indestructible and impenetrable. By combinations of atoms it was proposed to explain the infinite variety of things, together with all the movements and transformations which they are capable of undergoing. The result was a completely new cosmogony: a world of eternal atoms, unchangeable and indestructible, endowed with a vortex of undetermined origin which whirls them through the infinite void and causes them to collide and combine at haphazard. Nothing is created, nothing disappears; everything goes through a process of unceasing generation and decay. A selective process which brings together atoms of a similar shape and size produces all compound things, the earth and the stars. The soul itself is a product of the atoms, and is distinguishable from the body only by being composed of extremely mobile and spherical atoms whose organs are impinged upon by images. The gods themselves were fashioned in the same way as everything else, and play no part in the organization of things. Here once more the theory of man's origins forms a part of cosmogony.

In brief, according to a maxim quoted by Diogenes Laertius: "Everything arises from necessity, nothing is generated from the void, nothing returns to the void." This necessity is identified with the primal vortex which combines and separates the elements. Further than this it is impossible to go. Cicero says in so many words: "Democritus considers that this motion of the atoms is to be understood as eternal and due to no antecedent principle."

Such is the mechanistic explanation of the universe. Invented in the fifth century B.C. by Democritus, a contemporary of Hippocrates and also of Socrates (whom he refused to meet) this over-simple theory was adopted by Epicurus (341–270) and transmitted by him across the years to the Latin poet Lucretius (c. 98–53). With adaptations it remains the doctrine of contemporary materialism, though modern atomic physics has brought about important modifications. From the meta-physical point of view the theory presents two weaknesses: (1) eternal motion, and (2) the subjection of everything to chance.

THE COSMOGONY OF PLATO

Very different is the teaching of Plato (427–347), perhaps the greatest philosophical genius the world has ever known.

No attempt can here be made to expound the philosophy of Plato, comprising as it does a whole world of ideas.

We shall confine ourselves to his cosmogony, in so far as it includes his theory of the origins of man.

First of all, we must remind ourselves that we possess forty-three works of Plato, thirty of which are judged to be genuine. This very abstruse body of writing, cast mostly in dialogue form, reflects the inner development of its author's thought. Plato never ceased to reflect, to question his ideas, to revise and clarify them. It is above all in his latest works that we must seek the last word of his philosophy, of which the following is a very brief summary.

At the outset Plato aims, by the employment of bold dialectics, at transcending simple sense data. In his famous allegory of the cave he shows us men as the slaves of their senses, like prisoners in a cave. The world which our material eyes perceive is no more than a prison for the mind. What we take for reality is nothing more than shadows cast on the wall of the cave. However, by the exercise of thought we can and ought to escape from the cave. The science of numbers and of geometrical figures can help us on the way to rising above the visible world. Step by step we ascend towards the *Ideas* of things, until we reach the *Idea of the Good*, which is the sun of the intellectual world. In it alone is to be found the cause of everything that is just, of everything that is beauti-ful, of everything that is good. The Idea of the Good is there-fore both the dispenser and the ultimate explanation of the truth. And it is in and by that Idea that we must attain to the rule of all conduct, both private and public. This ascent of all things towards God, who is their author, is called dialectic. The Good is also the One. It is what we call God. "Every intelligible being", says Plato in one of the most powerful of his dialogues, "derives not only its intelligibility from the Good but also its being and essence, although the Good itself is not essence, but far exceeds both essence and intelligence in dignity and power" (*Republic*, VI, 509B).

It follows that nothing is left to chance. We are at the opposite pole from the atomistic materialism of Democritus. According to Plato, the Good is the supreme and sole cause of all things. The Good is inexhaustible reality, infinite riches, absolute and universal wisdom: it is the reason which controls the universe, and the source from which our own reason is derived. That things should be understandable by our minds is a marvel; but our minds were designed for that very purpose. The Good is omnipresent in the variety of individual forms. It governs all things without merging with them: Plato is in no sense a pantheist. The Good, being of an absolute purity and perfection, is other than the things which it governs and arranges, and remains transcendent to them. In other words, the cause is distinct from its effects, though not unrelated to them. The Good is therefore both transcendent to, and immanent in things: it is immanent because it is transcendent.

Such is the God of Plato. An almost infinite distance separates us from the grandiose speculations of the anthropomorphic mythologies discussed in the first chapter. The genius of Plato raises him far above the religious traditions of his country and age. Unlike Democritus, whose childish atomism simplifies everything and always reduces the higher to the lower, Plato has a deep awareness of the complexity of things, of the reality of the unseen, and of the power of ideas.

It is true that Plato presents us with no explicit theory of man's origin. It is among the characteristic features of the system expounded in his immortal dialogues that we must look for his views on the subject under discussion.

In the first place, Plato sees in man nothing but the soul. For him, the body is no more than a temporary prison. It is the soul alone which constitutes a human being. For Plato, therefore, the theory of man's origin reduces to the theory of the origin of the soul.

Now, according to Plato, it is impossible to understand anything about the world in which we live unless we first fix our eyes on God. It is from God that all things proceed.

There is in us a divine principle which will return to God after death. This divine principle is our soul. The soul is made for the contemplation of God, once it is freed from the agitations, the fears, the sorrows and the desires of earthly life.

With Plato, therefore, we have travelled a long way from the childish notions of God contained in the popular religions and in the traditional theogonies and mythologies. It is true that Plato himself sometimes has recourse to myths of his own invention, but they are of a quite new kind and far more impressive than those of his predecessors. Among these myths may be included the famous allegory of the cave, quoted above, as well as the myth of the demiurge, to be discussed below.

What is certain is that the God of Plato is very close to the Christian Trinity. He is the One, he is the Good, he is absolute and perfect Being. He is the source of wisdom, justice, science and beauty. He is the principle and the end of all things.

In him, therefore, all things dwell; from him all things proceed. In him man, like all the rest of creation, had his origin. But how? That is the question we must now answer.

One of the most famous doctrines of Platonic philosophy is the theory of *Ideas*. Plato teaches that God made all things according to eternal models, called by Plato the *Ideas* of things, which are infinitely more real than the individual things which copy them.

Nowhere, it is true, does Plato express the view, shared later on by St Augustine and by Malebranche, that the Ideas are simply the ideas of God. But nothing in his writings forbids us to believe that the Idea-types of things are in point of fact the thoughts of God. When Plato in the *Laws* says that "God is the measure of all things", in opposition to the teaching of the sophist Protagoras (485–411) that "Man is the measure of all things", he appears to be asserting that the Idea-types are the children of God himself.

Thus already in Plato are to be found those great doctrines which were to be worked out by medieval Christian philosophy, and to become the philosophical basis of Christian doctrine. It is true that Plato contains no clear expression of the principle of creation *ex nihilo*. But there will be no great difficulty in proving that all things, by virtue of their being ideas of God, are pre-existent in the Word, and that the creature differs substantially from uncreated Being; though being "like" him in that he partakes of him.

The philosophy of Plato undoubtedly constitutes one of the greatest achievements of human thought. Certain Fathers of the Church, such as St Justin in the second century, have not hesitated to assert that Plato himself was inspired by God to construct a metaphysical system of such sublimity.

If an explanation be sought for the origin of so lofty a doctrine, one might venture to say that Plato effected a fundamental reconstruction of the Pythagorean theory of numbers. He saw very clearly that numbers are of a purely quantitative nature. And if the study of numbers and "figures" can and ought to help mankind in its efforts to escape from "the cave of the senses"—that dark and blind cave, in the words of St John of the Cross; if numbers and "figures" partake to some extent of the eternal and unchangeable, and consequently of the supra-sensible, then it behoves man to raise himself by their means to the *essences*, which for their part are by nature qualitative. Now the essences are the types of things, i.e. their "Ideas". These Ideas are eternal, and all depend on the Idea of the Good, which is God.

Our own souls are akin to the Ideas, since by means of thought they find them in everything. And they find them because they have lived with them from eternity in God, before descending into our bodies. And it is in this conception of the human soul that we must look for the best proof of its immortality.

It would, however, be going too far not to admit that Plato's philosophy, admirable as it is, contains certain obscurities, omissions and defects. Of these Plato himself was fully aware, as is proved by his constant revision of his doctrine. His views on God and on God's relation to the world received their final shape only in Christian metaphysics, when St Augustine showed that the Ideas were in God, and that the world was created by God. This, no doubt, is merely an interpretation; but it supplied something lacking to, and in a sense demanded by the Platonic philosophy.

As a conclusion to this all too brief summary, we can glance at Plato's explanation, in the *Timaeus*, of the way in which God created the world. Here we are told that the world was made by a demiurge working after the fashion of a crafts-man and poet who was also a father, as already stated in the *Politicus* (273, B). This demiurge worked with his eyes fixed on the eternal models or patterns which are the Ideas. The identity of this demiurge is not altogether clear, though we may conceive him to be a personification of the Idea of the Good, that is to say God himself. He apparently made not only things but their models, i.e. the Ideas, as well. This supreme artificer would therefore be the Idea of the Good in action. It is not altogether clear whether he is a true creator. Plato certainly says that all things, when acted upon by God, pass from non-being to being (*Sophist*, 265 C). But as in an-other dialogue he uses the same terms in reference to the poet's activity, it is doubtful whether we are to understand the creation of the world as a creation *ex nihilo*. Moreover, Plato's main concern is with the problem of evil. In order to acount for the existence of evil, Plato confronts the demiurge with a pre-existent material, which he also calls a blind neces-sity. Intelligence strives to subdue this necessity to the Good, but it resists; and this resistance is the cause of all evil. Does Plato mean that evil is intrinsically a defect inherent in nature? That would anticipate the Christian doctrine. But Plato has not clearly explained the opposition between intelligence and necessity. He certainly did not intend to suggest two rival divinities; but though he reduced matter to a kind of non-being, he did not succeed in avoiding a certain dualism. What he lacked was the idea of the adversary, that is Satan, himself also a creature of God, but a free and rebellious creature.

There is another obscurity in the theory, and that is the relation of the individual to the Ideas or forms. For example, is it the form of humanity which is in every human being, or are all human souls, being akin to the Ideas, themselves Ideas, in such a way that every human being is an immortal essence?

In spite of all its unexplained obscurities, the *Timaeus* must rank among Plato's major works. In it he provides under the cover of fiction (for Plato too can invent a myth) a veritable encyclopedia of contemporary Greek speculation in astronomy, mathematics, physics and medicine. What he clearly perceived was that *the origin of man is included in the origin of the universe*, and that anthropogony is a privileged chapter of cosmogony. Hence it may be said that the true aim of the *Timaeus* was to furnish a complete description of humanity, both in body and in soul.

THE INFLUENCE OF PLATONISM

It is impossible to exaggerate the influence of Plato and of his teaching on all subsequent systems, even on such as contradicted or opposed him. He was regarded as the champion in philosophy of the existence of God, identified with the Good, of the immortality of the soul, and of the need to imitate God in all things needful for the good life. All these doctrines were to be found in the latest of the Master's dialogues: the *Politicus*, the *Sophist*, the *Philebus*, the *Timaeus* and the *Laws*. St Augustine in the *City of God* (*De Civitate Dei*, 8, 8) says: "Plato is convinced that to philosophize is to love God."

Moreover, in the time of St Augustine Platonism had come

to be seen through the spectacles of Neoplatonism, which we shall discuss later, and included features borrowed from all the rival philosophies. Nevertheless, before St Augustine a number of Fathers of the Church had already evinced the liveliest admiration for Plato. We have mentioned that St Justin regarded him as inspired by the Logos. Athenagoras quotes him, and the great "Alexandrians" Clement and, above all, Origen find in him a constant source of inspiration. Later on, the following may be included in the ranks of Platonists: Eusebius, Methodius of Olympia, Gregory Nazianzen and Gregory of Nyssa, Evagrius and even Athanasius and Basil.

We must now consider this "Platonism" of the Fathers. It consists first of all in a certain vocabulary: philosophy is pursued as a science of *the invisible*, but an invisible which is more *real* than the visible, a science which ought to be love, whose object is "union with God". The body is compared to a prison, and the world to a cave. The soul is weighed down by the body; man must escape from this earth in order to rise aloft. The soul is the child of God. Contemplation and purification must be practised. For St Augustine it was Plato, as presented in Cicero's *Hortensius*, who revealed the reality of the immaterial world, and when Augustine comes to explain his conversion or expound the doctrine of angels, he has recourse to Platonic speculation on the "intelligible" world and the "Ideas".

The whole of Christian mysticism is influenced, through the pseudo-Dionysius otherwise known as Dionysius the Mystic, by Platonism.

We must, however, insist that the Fathers, and after them the great medieval theologians, took from Plato and Aristotle only so much as would square with the unquestionable doctrines of the Christian revelation. This is expressly stated by Augustine in the *City of God*: "It is certain that I borrow from the Platonists nothing which is contrary to Holy Writ" (*De Civitate Dei*, 8, 4, 9 and 10). Origen says the same: "One must believe only in such truth as is not at variance with any ecclesiastical and apostolic tradition" (*De Principiis*, I, 1).

In the Middle Ages the influence of Platonism was exercised through pseudo-Dionysius (who was confused with Dionysius the Areopagite), and through the Arab philosopher Avicenna. St Bonaventura was accounted a Platonist. St Thomas himself wrote a commentary on Dionysius the Mystic. Albertus Magnus went so far as to write: "It is certain that no man can perfect himself in philosophy without a knowledge of the two philosophies of Aristotle and Plato" (*Metaphysics*, I, tract. 5, cap. 15).

The Renaissance considered Plato the master-philosopher. His influence is clearly discernible in Petrarch. But Plato's most enthusiastic disciple was Marsiglio Ficino (1433–99), an excellent translator though a mediocre critic and derivative thinker. On the other hand the boldest Platonist of the Renaissance was Pico della Mirandola (1463–94), who attempted to reconciliate Plato with Aristotle, and subsequently Platonism with Christianity.

Speaking generally, it may be said that the Augustinians were saturated in Platonism, in contrast with the Thomists and above all with the Nominalists.

ARISTOTLE ON THE ORIGINS OF MAN

The names of Aristotle and Plato are, so to speak, inseparable one from the other. They are at the same time complementary and opposed. Plato may be called the spirit of intuition, Aristotle the spirit of reason. The very word "dialectic" carries different meanings in Plato and in his disciple Aristotle. For Plato, dialectic is an ascent, by successive leaps and flashes of intuition, from sensible things to invisible things and to God. For Aristotle, dialectic is simply the art of reasoning, and reasoning consists in the *search for causes*.

Aristotle (384–322), though indulging in none of the superb flights of his master, whose teaching he ended by sharply criticizing, nevertheless drew from Plato his vital inspiration, and particularly for the doctrine taught by both that *the true reality is the invisible*, that God is the supreme Good, and that all things depend on him alone. Aristotle was in all things the champion of the "golden mean", of common sense, close and exact reasoning, flawless logic, and of what has been called "eurythmy".

Since we are here concerned only with the problem of man's origin, we shall confine ourselves to Aristotle's cosmogony. But it is essential first of all to recall the decisive contribution made to general science by this great thinker through his theory of causes.

No knowledge, we have already said, is possible unless it be "knowledge of causes". It is impossible to explain the origins of man without specifying their causes. But what do we mean when we speak of "causes"? It is due to the instinctive need to trace out causes that man has at all times speculated on the origins of the world and of himself. Yet frequently he has not taken into account *all the causes*, but has confined his attention to only a few of all those which have actually been in operation.

Aristotle constructed a complete theory of causes. He distinguished five kinds: *material*, or what a thing is made of; *formal*, or how a thing is made and constituted according to its own genus and species; *exemplary*, or according to what pattern it is made; *efficient*, whereby it passes from the state of non-being to that of being; and *final*, the ultimate reason for which it is made.

It is clear that a complete description of anything must comprise the following items: (1) What were the elements which entered into its composition, (2) what was the particular model on which it was made, (3) what agency brought it into existence, and (4) what was the object of this agency in bringing it from non-being into being?

It was through the omission of one or other of these causes that the explanations put forward by the ancient philosophers fell short. When Thales of Miletus or Anaximander or Anaximenes tell us what the world is made of—whether of water, or the unlimited, or air, or (as Heraclitus maintained) of fire—

it is obvious that they are referring solely to the material cause. They are therefore neglecting the four most important causes, viz. the formal, the exemplary, the efficient and the final.

Similarly when Pythagoras explains everything by the harmony of numbers, he is no doubt attempting to give the *formal* causes of things, but fails to explain their inner nature and specific qualities. Furthermore he omits the final, the efficient and the exemplary causes.

It is unnecessary to refer to the atomism of Democritus, identical, as has been pointed out, with that of Epicurus, Lucretius and our modern materialists; for their theory of eternal atoms in an external vortex amounts in reality to a negation of causality. The atoms and the vortex are both un-caused, the inter-collision of the atoms is governed by chance, which is the absence of causality. Such a philosophy, in Aristotle's and our own view, amounts to the negation of philosophy, which consists, we repeat, in "knowledge of causes".

To have brought these considerations into the highest prominence constitutes Aristotle's greatest contribution to human thought. No one has given better expression to the very requirements of the human intellect. Henri Bergson, a modern thinker who was, like Plato, in some sort the spirit of intuition, says, in his *Creative Evolution*, of the philosophy of Aristotle: "After eliminating everything derived from poetry, religion and social environment, as well as from a somewhat rudimentary physics and biology, we are left with the grand framework of a metaphysics which, I am convinced, *is the natural metaphysics of the human intellect.*"

When we speak of the Perennial Philosophy, we cannot fail to think in the first place of Aristotle and Plato. When St Thomas says: *Philosophus ait*, "the Philosopher says", by "the Philosopher" he means Aristotle.

Aristotle has, however, been criticized for reducing every-thing to what can be expressed in analysis and discourse, and for having neglected everything which is not amenable to analysis and discourse.

Above all, he has been reproached for entertaining such a lofty idea of God that he has ended by isolating God from the world. He will not allow God to know everything that happens on earth for fear of disturbing his happiness and tranquillity. He will not admit that God, *qua* efficient cause, created the world, since by so doing God would, so to speak, have "soiled his hands". It is true that he has the loftiest conception of God. It is a splendid thing when he says of God: "Such is the Principle from which both Heaven and Nature depend." St Thomas, who quotes this saying, hastens to add that by these words Aristotle has asserted the dependence of the world on this Principle (Ia, Q.44, art. 1). St Thomas is correct in one sense, but on closer examination we are astonished to discover that Aristotle's God is only the *final*, but by no means the *efficient* cause of the world and of man.

For Aristotle, God is pure Act and pure Intelligence, and hence the transcendent end of all that is. By his mere existence he draws all things to him, since he is the supreme Good, and the Good is defined as "that which all things desire". God is indeed the Prime Mover, but only inasmuch as he is the final end. No movement can take place without a purpose: a purposeless movement is inherently absurd. The reasons for a movement must consequently be sought for in the innate aspirations of the mover. The prime mover moves things only by virtue of being God. It is surprising to find that pure Act is incapable of acting, yet this is what Aristotle maintains: "To that Being which is the best and the most perfect must belong the Good without any kind of action" (*De Caelo*, II, 12). Contrast this with the saying of Christ: "My Father has never ceased working, and I too must be at work" (John 5. 17). For Aristotle, the divine perfection is incompatible with, at any rate, action from the outside. It is pure Act, in so far as it is infinite, unceasing and eternal Thought, never passing beyond the "potentiality of acting"; but it never commits itself to external action. Therefore for Aristotle creation, let alone creation *ex nihilo*, was inadmissible. For the very reason that God is perfect, he cannot be an efficient cause. In effect, before creating he would have had to be in a state of "potentiality" with respect to the creation. Now in pure Act there is no "potentiality" nor, as we have seen, any possible transition from "potentiality to act". On this point, it need hardly be said, the great Aristotelians of the Middle Ages were to correct and amplify Aristotle, or sometimes to content themselves with the belief that they were interpreting him, which was not always the case.

For Aristotle, the only aim worthy of God is self-contemplation. But the world's aim is likewise to contemplate God. He is thus the instigator of an eternal movement at the heart of eternal matter, which yearns towards him and takes on, in the course of its journey and in accomplishment of its aim, those forms or virtualities which lie within it in a state of "potentiality". The world is explicable by the movement of love which urges it towards God. Finally, the world is wholly dependent on God, for without him the eternal matter would be nothing, and would remain in the state of "potentiality" or "possibility". Matter proceeds to action, and to all the successive "acts" which constitute its movement towards God, only under the pressure of its longing for God. One might therefore say (and this appears to be the opinion of St Thomas) that God, by virtue of being a final cause, is also *an efficient cause*. What is certain is that the world depends wholly on him, that all things find their explanation in him, and that the ultimate ground both of things and of man in particular is God. This conception was adopted by Christianity as a prime truth: it is the *final cause* referred to in the opening words of the Catechism:

Q. "Why did God make you?"

A. "God made me to know him, to love him and serve him in this world, and to be happy with him for ever in the next."

Similarly, it is upon the conception of a *final cause* that

Ignatius Loyola built the *Foundation* of his famous "Spiritual Exercises".

Towards the end of his life Aristotle seems to have moved towards a kind of pantheistic naturalism. When he speaks of "nature" he seems to be anticipating the later conception of "nature" as a kind of divine being. In his latest works he constantly associated God and nature in the creation and explanation of the world (*De Caelo*, I, 4), so that one is tempted to conclude that for him God is distributed through the world and is perhaps no more than omnipresent divinity. It must not be forgotten, however, that he had always placed the unique Thought above all things, equating it with the Prime Mover. We may therefore venture to believe that he remained faithful to his fundamental theism.

THE STOICS AND THE ORIGINS OF MAN

Although Plato and Aristotle represent the twin summits of Greek philosophy, mention must be made of the Stoic School. The leading philosophers of this school were, it is true, strictly speaking foreigners, though citizens of the Hellenic world. Zeno of Citium, the founder of the school, was born in Cyprus. His successor Cleanthes came from the Troad, while Chrysippus, whose influence in the Stoic School was so great that he was called the "second founder", came from St Paul's country of Cilicia.

Stoic cosmogony can be summed up in a few words: All things are ruled by destiny, fate, necessity, defined by Chrysippus as "a certain disposition of all things, linking them together for all eternity". Fate explains all things. Fate is God, but a God who is the primal element, at the same time the fire or breath and the soul or mind of the world. Fate is truth, it is nature, the inner power which everything obeys. All things are ordered, controlled and governed to the last detail by fate. From this doctrine the Stoics derived the interesting conception of *Providence*. The world does not pursue a random course: it is regulated in accordance with an all-seeing providence which permeates all its parts, and acts within it as a directing principle, like the soul in man. In this sense fate may be called the *Logos* of the universe. But this Logos is not only a ruling but a generative power. It is the Logos that disposes and arranges all things, acting through seminal principles which bring forth all things with their characteristic qualities in due season. This force, which constitutes and holds together the universe, is at the same time the *matter* and the *form* of every individual thing. Stoicism thus arrives at a kind of naturalistic pantheism, in which God is indistinguishable from, and identified with, his handiwork. *The individual is swallowed up in the whole.* In vain did the Stoics, like the Jansenists after them, strive to preserve individual freedom by magnifying the human will. Seneca, Epictetus and Marcus Aurelius sometimes speak in almost Christian tones; yet never did they succeed in explaining how everything can be necessary and dependent on fate without destroying the moral responsibility of the individual. Even our admiration for Cleanthus' famous Hymn to Zeus cannot blind us to the harsh law of universal necessity and Stoic fatalism.

In this celebrated hymn Zeus is addressed as "the omnipotent eternal Being, the author and lord of creation; who directs all things in accordance with the Law; *from whom we come*; to whom the whole of this universe is obedient as it revolves round the earth, going whither he leads it and submitting to his guidance".

There is undoubtedly a certain beauty in these words, and in comparison with Aristotle one may say that real progress has been made. Aristotle claimed in effect that it is better for God to be ignorant of certain things which might disturb his peace and perfection. Cicero, on the other hand, defines the Stoic doctrine in the following terms: "They hold that the world is guided by the power of the gods in such a way that it is, so to speak, the common city and possession of men and gods alike, and that each one of us is a portion of it." Here we see another example of the way in which a theory of man's

origin penetrates a cosmogony, of which it becomes the fulfilment and the crown.

Thus, for the Stoics, all wisdom and all morality consist in
following and imitating God, and in conforming to his law.
All the thinkers we have so far considered, with the exception of the atomistic materialists, employ very nearly the
same language. It will be for Christianity to add its dazzling
rule of conduct: to imitate God is simply to imitate Jesus
Christ, God made Man for the salvation of all men.

NEOPLATONIC COSMOGONY AND THEORY OF THE ORIGINS OF MAN

We conclude this survey of the major Greek philosophies
with a brief sketch of Neoplatonism. Here we make the
acquaintance of a very great name, that of Plotinus, whose
disciples Porphyry, Proclus and Iamblichus were far inferior
to their master. Plotinus was born at Lycopolis in Egypt in
204 B.C., and studied at Alexandria under Ammonius Saccas.
This thinker inspired him with a kind of mystical eclecticism,
a blend of the philosophies of Plato, Aristotle and the Stoics,
but aimed solely at the perfecting of the soul.

Plotinus added depth to the teachings of his master, and
himself made a number of disciples, by whom he was pas-
sionately admired and revered. His teachings are contained in
a collection of fifty-four tracts divided into six groups of nine,
and were hence called *Enneads*.

At the summit of things Plotinus places the One, which
engenders *Nous* (Mind or Spirit), who is at the same time
Being, the Intelligible, and Thought. *Nous* in its turn engenders the *Soul*.

But this triune God cannot remain alone. There is therefore "necessarily in that which issues from him, in that which
flows from him and separates itself from him, a final product
after which no more generation takes place: and that product
is *evil*. There must necessarily be beings which come after the
first being: consequently there is a last term. This is *matter*,

which in no way participates in the first term. Such is *the necessity* of evil."[1]

Accordingly the world is necessary, but evil is also necessary. There is no world without matter, and matter is "by nature evil".

It is necessary that all possible forms should manifest themselves, setting out from the One. Matter is situated at the lowest point of these "processions". For man, all perfection consists in freeing himself from matter, in order to ascend once more to the One. According to this doctrine, the origin of man is located in the path of the "processions" from the One, while his destiny is located on the *ascent* towards the One.

Since all things proceed from the One, all things must of necessity reflect the One. The world of bodies is the expression of intelligence, in that it forms a universe of interconnected parts. "All beings", says Plotinus, "hold together, and compose a marvellous symphony; one proceeds from another, even from its opposite" (*Enneads*, IV, 4, 38). Thus "the universe is full of signs, and wise is he who can infer one thing from another." Finally, Plotinus sums up his philosophy in the following passage of capital importance: "Since this world is a living thing which contains all living things, since it derives its being and its manner of being from another world which is related to Spirit, it follows of necessity that the exemplary universe must be located in Spirit; and Spirit is that intelligible world which Plato, in the *Timaeus*, calls 'Life in itself' " (*Enneads*, V, 9, 9).

Plotinus propounds a "pan-cyclic" theory of the universe. The Good or the One is at the centre. *Nous* is the first circle, and is the image of the Good. Soul is the second circle. The other beings form the whole sphere of the world, which extends round the centre and revolves about it. Perfection for each individual being consists in ascending once more to its centre, which is the Good. The realm of matter is the furthest point to which Thought is diffused. It marks the end of the

[1] Cf. *Enneads*, I, 7–8.

path which Thought, within itself and starting from the One, follows with the aim of providing itself with images.

The dualism of good and evil, of soul and body is not the meeting of two opposite principles, but the conflict between two orders, the second of which derives from the first its very quality of contrariety. Strictly biological life and spiritual life face in opposite directions, but spiritual perfection consists precisely in freeing oneself from the biological, in order to develop the spiritual life.

Thus in Plotinus we see a dualism ceaselessly reappearing but always overcome. It is the dualism, so well defined by St Paul, between the flesh and the spirit.[1]

From the account of the various Greek philosophies we can foresee that Christianity found much in them worth retaining. It made its selection among the various doctrines, and was inevitably eclectic in such a wide field of choice. To say that Christianity became hellenized sounds perhaps like a reproach. In reality it would be praise, for to hellenize was to espouse all in human thought that was most rational, exalted, solid and durable. Yet Christianity was to add to Greek philosophy a new note, to stamp it as it were with a divine seal. To this point we return in our last chapter, when we contrast Christian teaching on the origins of the world and of man with the ideas held successively by the mythologies and philosophies on the one hand, and the discoveries of modern science on the other.

A SKETCH OF INDIAN AND CHINESE PHILOSOPHIES

We might at this point have brought to a close our account of the philosophical solutions of the problem of origins, since Christianity has undergone no influence whatever from the philosophies of India and of the east in general. But nowadays the western mind, steeped as it is in the Christian tradition,

[1] Further details on this subject may be found in the volumes of this series dealing with the origins and development of Christian philosophy.

has been to a certain extent attracted by these philosophies, with which we have recently come into contact. A few words must therefore be said about them.

In India, a situation arose somewhat similar to that which we observed in Greece. Although in Persia, Egypt and Assyro-Babylonia it proved impossible to construct a philosophy distinct from religion, it is nevertheless permissible to speak of a Hindu wisdom disentangled from the primitive myths. The Rig-Veda contained traditional conceptions handed down from time immemorial. But at the very time when Greek philosophy was shaking itself free from mythology, the brahmanic Upanishads, probably committed to writing between the seventh and fifth centuries B.C., were giving a new expression to Hindu speculation. All things are presided over by Brahma, the self-existent Absolute who created all the gods and entrusts them with the government of the world.[1]

In Jainism, on the other hand, there is no place for a divine cosmogony, since the universe is conceived as having neither beginning nor end.

Jainism, said to have been founded by Vardhamāna in the sixth century B.C., provides for two eternal substances, one inert and gross, composing the inanimate part of the world, the other animate, composing the souls, from those of the plants to those of the gods. These souls are indestructible and eternally individual. All the perishable forms which we see in the world are produced by an eternal and irresistible force, which is the consequence of the previous acts of every individual. *The souls undergo a slow process of evolution, passing from vegetable to animal, from animal to man, and from man to god.* The contemplation and mortifications which should accompany this process afford the best means of making the ascent at the end of which man attains to Nirvana. In this doctrine, the theory of the origins of man forms but one chapter in the theory of the origin of all things.

Buddhism, which traces its origin to the partly mythical

[1] On this subject see the volume on Hinduism by J. Lemaître in the present series.

person of the Buddha, whose real name was Sakya-Muni (second half of sixth century B.C.), is principally a method of working through the series of transmigrations, by means of a rule of life devoted to meditation, chastity, mendicancy and preaching. If we attempt to discover the beliefs of Buddhism concerning the origins of man, we are driven back on the brahmanism which preceded it. Buddhism asserts the eternity and indestructibility of the basic material, and the action of an inevitable mechanical law, entirely independent of the divine will, which binds, separates or combines the elements in such a way as to produce the constituents of the universe. From eternity, worlds are born, grow, decline and perish, only to be born again. The soul of living creatures is trapped in this universal process of transformation. The problem for every soul is to escape from it. It is *yoga* which provides the means of escape by putting an end to both vices and virtues. By this means man attains to Nirvana, as in Jainism, though the Buddhist Nirvana appears to be identical with non-being, since it abrogates the law of transmigration which is the root of all evil.

These systems reveal both the astonishing gift of the peoples of India for appreciating the pangs of universal dissolution, and the longing for eternal peace which is happiness itself, together with an obvious incapacity to solve the problems raised by this unhappy state of affairs. The thinkers—or rather the dreamers—of India attach no importance to any conceptual representation of the universe. All that matters is to free oneself from concepts, as well as from desire and action. It follows that Hinduism abounds in the most contradictory statements. "To Indian orthodoxy," it has been said, "metaphysics is a closed book."[1]

To a Hindu, the existence of God, the doctrine of creation, the very existence of the soul are purely academic questions, useless for salvation, which is achieved by "disciplined breathing".

[1] La Vallée-Poussin, "Le Bouddhisme et les Religions de l'Inde", in *Christus* (Paris, 1916), p. 414.

Similar features are found in the "wisdom of China". As we have already remarked, the ancient Chinese religion possessed neither a doctrine of creation nor myths of the origin of the world.

The principal Chinese thinkers were Lao-Tse, and after him Confucius (Kung-fu-tse) (551–478 B.C.).

So far as one can reconstruct the doctrine underlying Chinese speculation, it appears that Chinese philosophers were struck by the interdependence of all living things and natural events and phenomena, which gave rise to an harmoniously ordered cosmos to which man must submit and adjust his behaviour.

On this condition alone can the individual for his part cooperate with the cosmic order. By doing so he may even succeed in gaining control over the forces of nature through magic and divination, thereby making himself to a certain extent master of the universal flux.

But the Chinese mind, like the Hindu, recoils from anything conceptual, abstract, quantitative and mechanical. It denies causality, but recognizes mysterious connections between things, whose secret power must be grasped and exploited by man through the practice of magic.

Even in our own day, in Tibet, this aspiration after the mastery of things by magical practices is held in honour.

From all this we must conclude that the west was most fortunate in not depending on the meagre obscurities of these Oriental philosophies. Instead, she found herself in the direct line of Greek thought, so rich and various and above all so stimulating, in the sense that it fostered the thirst for knowledge and gave birth to science, whose children we are.

GENERAL SURVEY

There are two reasons why we need not pursue our search for the origins of man among the philosophies. The first is, that the Christian philosophies which succeeded the ancient philosophies were content, so far as the origins of man are concerned, with the facts provided by biblical revelation. Philosophy became the "handmaid of theology". Even when, as with St Thomas, it broke away in pursuit of its own life and methods, it remained in close contact with the teachings of theology, whose discipline and conclusions it adopted, while presenting them in philosophic or systematic form.

The second reason is, that modern philosophy has for the most part handed over to science the problem of human origins. Astronomy has ceased to be a branch of philosophy, and has taken over cosmogony. In our own times, as we shall see in the next chapter, palaeontology and prehistory have appropriated the problem of man's origins, and have no intention of relinquishing it.

Nevertheless, the philosophers retain the privilege of having their say (which they regard as the last word) on the problem of origins, by fitting man into the framework of the natural world. We can therefore attempt a general survey of the answers given by philosophy to the problem of man.

There have been, and still are, two ways of regarding man. Many thinkers, especially in ancient times, have regarded man as a static and quasi-extra-temporal *natural object*. A few of the ancients, and all the moderns, regard him as *a history*.

Plato saw man—that is to say the totality of souls—as an eternal and unchangeable essence. Souls, according to Plato, are akin to the Ideas, and the Ideas are eternal. This principle of the pre-existence of souls was taken over by Origen, and condemned by the Church along with other tenets of Origenism.

For Aristotle, man is still quasi-extra-temporal. The Prime Mover moves the world from all eternity. God is unaware of the world, nor did he create it. It follows, according to Averroës, that Aristotle is committed to the belief in an infinity of men, an infinity of souls, but all possessing one single mind, which alone is immortal. According to Averroës, Aristotle must therefore have denied personal immortality, as he denied providence.

The Stoics also appear to have envisaged man as a *natural*

object, and not as *a history*. On the other hand, in Neo-platonism and in the Hindu doctrine of transmigration we find a compromise between the two conceptions. All things end in an eternal immobility, but only after passing through a "history", that is, a series of preparations and metamorphoses or metempsychoses.

Modern philosophy holds a totally different view of man. Hegel sees man as part of an endless dialectical process, which is history itself, with its triadic movement of thesis, anti-thesis and synthesis. Karl Marx adopts the same point of view; though he twists it in the direction of evolutionary materialism. For Karl Marx and his disciples man is a history, and a meaningful history. The meaning of history moves towards the victory of the proletariat and the Communist idea.

Nowadays all the modern anthropological sciences accept the principle of evolution as a matter of course. It is no longer possible to regard man as a natural object, but only as a history, and even as the apex of history and universal evolution.

All this will become clear in the next chapter.

CHAPTER III

MODERN SCIENCE AND THE ORIGINS OF MAN: POSITIVE GENEALOGIES

THE COMING OF SCIENCE

Just as philosophy replaced poetry and mythology in explaining the origins of the world and of man, so has science for the last few centuries taken over the quest from philosophy.

Science differs from philosophy in that it is concerned not with the "final causes of things", but with their proximate and immediate causes. It refuses to go beyond the facts. A scientific fact is a fact of physical observation, a fact registered by the senses and by the innumerable instruments which man has called in to supplement his senses. The facts once observed and registered are subjected when possible to precise verification in the form of experiments. But science ventures beyond the facts in attempting to explain them. This she achieves by first framing hypotheses and then, after verification, giving them the force of laws if their validity as explanation is confirmed. From this it follows that a hypothesis leads on to fresh observations, and is thus a kind of working tool. But a hypothesis aspires to become a scientific law, and becomes one as soon as it has successfully passed the test of experiment which it has itself set in train.

This short account shows the gulf which separates science from mythology and even from philosophy. Mythology raises problems, for which it invents baseless solutions, regardless of the possibility of verification. It consists of groundless beliefs, which first philosophy and then science were obliged to destroy once and for all.

Philosophy, for her part, is more consistent. Consequently, confronted with the rise of science she offered a firmer and moreover entirely legitimate resistance. Contrary to the assertions of certain philosophers such as Auguste Comte and the Positivists, it is natural that philosophy and science instead of conflicting should join hands. Science remains incomplete and "in the air" so long as its enquiries are not extended by philosophy; while philosophy, for her part, cannot advance along the road leading to "the final causes of things" without relying on science and the special sciences.

With these distinctions in mind, we shall attempt to describe what science has to tell us about the origins of man and the world.

MAN'S PLACE IN THE UNIVERSE

The greatest change brought about by the advance of science lies in man's feelings regarding his place in the universe and his status in space and time.

It is principally astronomy that has transformed our picture of the world. For many centuries man saw himself at the centre of things. It was believed that the earth was a flat and motionless disk, round which the sun and the stars revolved. No one had ever calculated the distance from the earth of the sun, let alone of the stars, which were moreover believed to lie in the same curved plane, like gilded nails fixed on the inside of a dome. Until recent times it was almost impossible to believe that the earth was round, and that there was such a thing as "the antipodes", which could be imagined only as men with their heads below and their feet in the air. It was for this very reason that Christopher Columbus had such difficulty in gaining approval for his voyage to discover a westerly passage to China.

We recall the various stages in the conquest of the heavens by astronomy since Copernicus and Galileo. In ancient times Aristarchus had already propounded the heliocentric theory, but he had no followers.

Copernicus reverted to this theory. Galileo proclaimed the bankruptcy of geocentricism, and of the reigning Ptolemaic system. This was in the year 1609. He raised a storm of protest, and was even thrown into prison for his temerity. It took a century and a half for his ideas to win universal acceptance. But until the end of the eighteenth century astronomy confined its interest to the solar system. In the centre was the sun, and round it were the planets, among them the earth, revolving in accordance with the mathematical laws formulated by Newton and Laplace. However, at the beginning of the nineteenth century John Frederick Herschel applied himself to the problem of the stars, calculated their distances in collaboration with James South, and drew up a catalogue in 1825 in which he enumerated 2,306 nebulae, 525 of which were his own discovery. In 1838, thanks to the exact calculations of Frederick Bessel, it was proved that the stars were much further away than had been supposed, and that they formed a galaxy, the Milky Way, in which the sun was merely one modest star among the rest. Heliocentricism, the destroyer of geocentricism, was doomed in its turn. For the past century at least scientists have known that our solar system forms part of a much vaster system comprising a whole multitude of stars scattered at very varying distances from each other. Our galaxy, or Milky Way, however, was still presumed to contain all the stars in the firmament.

In 1918, American astronomer Harlow Shapley tried to measure this galaxy of stars. He arrived at the enormous figure of 300,000 light-years, each light-year representing in round figures six and a half billion miles. We know now that our galaxy measures only 80,000 light-years.

Shortly after the First World War the giant telescope at Mount Wilson in California came into action. This has a reflector 100 inches in diameter. A revolutionary advance in astronomy followed immediately. The telescope reached beyond the limits of the Milky Way, revealing brilliant and slightly elongated patches which could not possibly be single stars. They must therefore be "star-clusters", in other words more galaxies. The nebula or galaxy nearest to us was Andromeda, distant about 900,000 light-years.

Our conception of the universe has thus undergone many changes: first the earth, then the sun, and now our own Milky Way have been toppled from their thrones.

Such was the scientific position about the year 1925. The great astronomer Hubble, in his book *The Kingdom of the Nebulae* published in 1936, pictured the world as an unlimited archipelago of island-universes, isolated from each other and scattered at random beyond the reach of sight, up to the distance of at least 500 million light-years which was reckoned the extremest range of the hundred-inch telescope.

Now today these estimates are considered to be false, or at least grossly inaccurate. For in 1949 there came into service at Mount Palomar a giant telescope with a 200-inch reflector.[1] Since 1950 Walter Bade has been at the post of observation. By 1952 he was able to report to the Rome Congress of Astronomers that the world was far vaster than had been supposed. The nebula Andromeda must be placed at a distance of at least 1,500,000 light-years. The range-limit of the Mount Wilson telescope must be estimated at a thousand million light-years. More recently, as a result of further measurements, it has been suggested that the old distances may have to be doubled and even trebled.

Astronomers are inclined to believe in the existence of "galaxy-clusters", after the pattern of the "star-clusters". For example, the constellation Virgo is thought to be an agglomeration of six clusters of galaxies comprising some 2,500 galaxies.

In view of all this, what becomes of our poor little planet? What becomes of man? Our own galaxy is but an insignificant unit among a million, and in that galaxy our sun is but one insignificant star among its hundred thousand million fellows.

Hence the reflection of an astronomer on the subject of the importance of man in a universe of such a description:

[1] See the special issue of *The Scientific American* for September, 1956, devoted to astronomy.

"One must be the victim of incurable anthropocentrism to believe that the slightest importance attaches to the race of thinking microbes inhabiting an imperceptible globe revolving round this sun."[1]

It will of course be our business, when we come to compare doctrines in our concluding chapter, to offer a reply to this pessimistic opinion of the importance of man and of the soundness of our faith.

THE AGE OF THE WORLD AND THE AGE OF MAN

Astronomy not only succeeds in placing man in space, it also helps to place him in time. Nowadays, apparently, no one can be found to maintain that the world is without end; but it certainly had a beginning. Astronomy, basing itself on the fact of the recession of the stars, estimates that the whole of stellar matter could have been condensed, about five and a half thousand million years ago, into one single giant atom, which then exploded, and whose fragments, which form the galactic stars, are receding at a speed which can be fairly approximately calculated. The latest speed suggested is 70,500 miles per second!

Our earth, the result according to some of a contraction of the sun, or according to the new Cambridge school of a starburst, may be three billion (3,000,000,000) years old.

We shall see later that of these three billion man has been in existence for only 500,000 years.[2]

If we wish to understand how figures such as these have shattered the old conceptions, we have only to open Bossuet's celebrated *Discours sur l'histoire universelle*, published in 1681. This work, as we know, was written for the instruction of the French Dauphin, and consequently represented the last word of contemporary theology and science. It opens with the following sentence:

[1] Pierre Rousseau, "Dernière Image de l'Univers", in *La Revue de Paris*, June 1956, p. 127.
[2] These figures and those above are taken from *The Scientific American* for September, 1956.

"The first epoch presents you straightway with a magnificent spectacle: God creating the heavens and earth by his word, and making man in his image (Year of the world 1—Before Jesus Christ 4004). This is where Moses begins, who is the first historian, the noblest philosopher and the wisest law-giver."

The parenthesis is remarkable. In it Bossuet gives two dates: year of the world 1, and year 4004 B.C. It follows that man and the world are contemporaries to within a few days. In any case they belong to the same year, and that year is only 4004 years ago. It is not so very long ago that we used to sing in church at Christmas:

> More than four thousand years ago
> We were promised by the prophets...

All is changed now. The age of the world is totally different from the age of man. The earth, a fragment of sun or star, took about 1,500,000 years to cool. A crust formed: the astral phase of the planet was over. And at the end of this long period came the wonder of wonders—*the appearance of life*.

The first manifestations of life have probably left no trace. Then there began the *era of fossils*, i.e. those remains of living creatures which it is the task of the new science *palaeontology* to study, classify and name.

This science is based on the sub-division of geology known as stratigraphy. It is stratigraphy which has drawn up the chronology of the earth's past, which is divided into four periods called *Primary*, *Secondary*, *Tertiary* and *Quaternary*.

It was only during the last of these long periods that man made his appearance. In the course of these successive periods certain important facts assert themselves. In the first place, the forms of life have been constantly changing from age to age and assuming a rising curve. From the humblest and most rudimentary forms, life has steadily risen to richer, more complex, and often bulkier forms. This last feature, however, did not continue till the end, for it was in the secondary period, which began about 200 million years ago and lasted some 130 million years, that there lived on earth monsters of fearsome size and weight, destined in the event to disappear almost completely.

In the second place, from the outset we are confronted with a startling fact, known as the "acceleration of history". The fact is that the geological and palaeontological periods become progressively shorter. The primary period lasted three hundred and fifty million years, the secondary only one hundred and thirty million, and the tertiary seventy million. As the tertiary period will prove of great interest to us, its subdivisions should be noted: they are, from earliest to latest, the *eocene* (twenty-five million years); the *oligocene* (ten million years); the *miocene* (twenty million years); and the *pliocene* (fifteen million years). Lastly, the quaternary period has already lasted about a million years. And it is towards the middle of this period that man makes his appearance.

Of the two facts set forth above, it is the first which is the more important. It has indeed given rise to a theory of the greatest interest, known as *evolutionism*, which we must take into account in what follows.[1]

PREHISTORY

Palaeontology must be accounted a relatively new science, since the French scientist Georges Cuvier (1769–1832) has been called its "father" by virtue of his famous book *Recherches sur les ossements fossiles* (1821–4). Though it has always been considered an absorbing pursuit, there is one of its branches, Prehistory, which, more thrilling than all the others, has in its turn been promoted to the status of an independent or at least distinct science. This designation is applied to the history of mankind as revealed by his surviving fossil remains. In other words, it is the *science of human origins*. Clearly it must find a place in our present survey.

In prehistory we include all those events relating to man

[1] This theory is of such great interest that a special volume of this series is devoted to it.

which took place before the invention of writing. The science is still in its infancy. Our museums are crammed with fossil remains. Scientists are hard at work on them. The liveliest discussion continues unabated. And not without reason. Human skeletons are not all of the same age. A comparison between them reveals many differences. And these differences become even more marked when they are compared with modern man. But this is not the most exciting discovery. Side by side with undoubtedly human skeletons, related fossils have been found, confronted with which science hesitates before pronouncing on the disquieting question, "man or animal?"

It was first of all necessary to set up a certain criterion. The first scientific prehistorians started from the principle that the distinguishing mark of man is intelligence. Even if we grant the animals a certain intelligence, it never, as with man, attains to the level of reasoning, of deduction or induction. In practice, the proof of intelligence at the human level is human industry. When our excavations turn up an artefact, we may be sure of being in presence of a *man-made product*. Basing himself on these facts of prehistory as professed for more than sixty years, the philosopher Henri Bergson in his fine book *Creative Evolution* (1906) wrote as follows:

"To what date do we trace the appearance of man on the earth? To the time when the first weapons and the first tools were made. We can still remember the famous dispute which raged round Boucher de Perthes' discovery in the Moulin-Quignon quarry. The question at issue was whether the objects found were genuine axes or fragments of accidentally broken flints. But no one for one instant doubted that, if they were axes, one was in the presence of intelligence, and more specifically of human intelligence."

Why was no doubt possible on this point? Because no animal has ever succeeded in making a tool.

Nowadays Bergson may be outdated on many points with which we have to deal. But the principle which he enunciated in the words we have quoted was not his own discovery. It lay at the roots of all prehistorical research and, as we shall see later, remains in force to this day.

The latest researches in "animal psychology" have not affected the validity of this principle. The difference between man and ape is particularly apparent in the treatment accorded to them. In furtherance of research into this distinction, the American biologist Yerkes in 1930 set up a special laboratory in Florida, now under the direction of Dr Karl S. Lashley, for the study of the biology of the primates. Today it houses sixty chimpanzees, apes closest to man from the point of view of intelligence. They are taught tricks, undergo tests, and are trained to compete for appropriate prizes. Experiments are made to determine how much they retain of the knowledge they have acquired, with the following results: like human beings they vary greatly in intelligence. Some are ready learners, but all are lacking in method. They take no interest in what they have learnt, and are incapable of applying it.

Their intelligence rises to "association", never to "deduction" or "induction", never to reasoning. Thus Portia, the female chimpanzee in the Yerkes laboratory who is the cleverest at solving her little problems, frequently scores between ten and eighteen correct answers in a row, which she follows up with an unbroken series of glaring errors.[1]

The gulf between man and animal is therefore immense. The mere fact that we subject these apes to every kind of experiment, even including surgical operations (lobotomy), for the benefit of mankind, is sufficient proof that we do not treat them as "persons" having rights and duties.

Having made this point quite clear we may proceed to the study of earliest man.

EARLIEST MAN

Until recently it was possible to say that the oldest tools

[1] For the Yerkes laboratory, see an article by George W. Gray in *The Scientific American* for February, 1955.

discovered were not associated with any human remains. At a quite recent date (1955) Professor Arambourg discovered human bones in conjunction with primitive tools at Ternifine in Algeria, a few miles from Mascara. Until then no progress had been made since the days of Boucher de Perthes. Born in Rethel in 1788, he was a customs officer at Abbeville. With his friend Camille Picard, whose name will always be remembered in association with his, he unearthed in 1844 in a quarry at Chelles, in the department of Seine-et-Marne, some carved flints which appeared to him to be the undoubted work of an extremely primitive human being, much older at any rate than the biblical Adam who lived only 4004 B.C. He at once announced that he had found traces of tertiary man. These consisted of almond-shaped stones, with one rounded end for holding in the hand, and a cutting end for use as a tool or weapon. These flints resembled either daggers or spear-points, or scrapers or chisels. They were not all deposited at the same geological level, and presumably dated from different epochs. We had here, Boucher de Perthes was convinced, undoubted traces of the oldest human activity, although in the same deposits no human remains were to be found.

The most violent controversy immediately raged round this discovery. Official science rose in protest. Boucher de Perthes' first reports to the Académie des Sciences met with a hostile reception. But thanks to the support of English geologists he succeeded in winning acceptance for his theory of the existence in very ancient times of what is now called Chellean Man, from the name of the parish where the discovery was made.

But how old was Chellean Man?

THE PROBLEM OF DATING

For the past century all the efforts of the prehistorians have been directed towards establishing an accurate chronology extending from Chellean Man to the present day. What we can be certain of is that Chellean Man belongs not, as Boucher de Perthes supposed, to the tertiary but to the quaternary period. At the same time the quaternary, which succeeded the *pliocene* and has lasted for about a million years, has shown great variations in climate. Quite recently the discovery in the Siberian peninsula of Taimir of a mammoth in a perfect state of preservation, embedded in a block of ice and dead before it had time to digest its last meal, has strengthened the theory that during the quaternary epoch the position of the terrestrial poles has shifted. This mammoth, the contents of whose stomach it was found possible to analyse, had eaten the leaves of a tropical plant. The fact that it was embedded whole in a huge globe of ice which preserved it intact, presupposes some sudden catastrophe which can have consisted only in a change in the climate of its habitat from the hottest to the coldest found on earth.

Moreover, there are many other indications which prove that the quaternary age was marked not only by immensely long periods during which our now temperate regions were extremely hot, but by periods of intense glaciation such as have left widely dispersed traces in the "moraines" formed by a subsequent thaw, to be found for instance in the Dombes region of Burgundy.

During each glacial period an ice-cap, hundreds and perhaps thousand of yards thick, covered the approaches to the French and Pyrenean Alpine systems; and the same is true of Scandinavia, North Germany and Siberia.

Attempts have been made to measure the duration of each interglacial and glacial period, with the following results:

1. Glacial: *Günz* (a tributary of the Danube)—45,000 years.
2. First Inter-glacial: *Günz-Mindel*—65,000 years.
3. Second Glacial: *Mindel* (a Rhine valley)—45,000 years.
4. Second Inter-glacial, which lasted for the enormous period of 190,000 years.
5. Third Glacial: *Riss* (a tributary of the Isar)—45,000 years.
6. Third Inter-glacial—65,000 years.

7. Fourth and last Glacial: *Würm* (a stream north of Munich)—95,000 years.

This was succeeded by a period of final evolution which lasted 35,000 years. We are now, and have been for about 15,000 years, in the post-glacial period.

If Chellean Man belongs to a hot, that is an inter-glacial period, it is important to decide in which period to place him. Marcellin Boule suggested the third Riss-Würm inter-glacial, which would put his date at between 100,000 and 200,000 B.C. On the other hand Abbé Breuil, a staunch defender of Chellean Man's antiquity, has profoundly modified Boule's conclusions. The Abbé carried out a thorough survey of the sedimentary complex in which the oldest remains of human handicraft were discovered, and brought to light the various layers which can be identified throughout the length of the River Somme. As a result, he has claimed to establish that a number of inter-glacial periods overlap in these deposits. A tentative figure of 600,000 years can be given for the earliest appearance of man in these regions. And although these figures have been disputed, there are today few prehistorians prepared to allow less than 400,000 years since the origin of mankind.

The presence of man in the first inter-glacial period in Europe is now agreed by nearly all the experts. The first real man takes his place beside the elephant of the Midi and the Etruscan rhinoceros, whose fossil species appear to have vanished during glacial period *Mindel*, 470,000 years ago.

It must, however, be emphasized that these figures cannot provide more than a scale of magnitude: they are approximate figures. The earliest date for the appearance of man cannot be determined to within 100,000 years. And the inevitable uncertainty as to date extends to most of the other findings of prehistory.

A contemporary expert in prehistory, M. André Varagnac, pointed this out in a recent book:

"Prehistorians and protohistorians are acquainted from

daily experience with the uncertainties of scientific opinion in their own special fields. They know that with every excavation they carry out, their findings will upset the convictions of their great predecessors. Now, every year hundreds of sites are excavated and thousands of reports published in more than twenty different languages. The result is that the task of striking even a provisional balance-sheet is enough to discourage even the boldest."[1]

A wide margin of latitude must therefore be allowed to the assertions of scientists.

All that we are about to say on this subject must therefore be provisional. Prehistory is still in the making. From it we must select only such facts as are by now established.

THE FACTS AS AT PRESENT KNOWN

At the present day we have at our disposal a large number of human fossils. The problem, however, is complicated by the simultaneous discovery of an even greater number of hominian or *hominidae* fossils, that is to say fossils akin to man.

Where does man begin? Where does the animal end? It is sometimes difficult to tell. But it is a striking fact that man makes his appearance in an animal environment closely related to him. In point of fact the entire animal kingdom is divided into two great branches, invertebrates and vertebrates. The vertebrates, to which we belong, are in their turn divided into classes. The highest of these classes consists of the mammals, who appeared towards the end of the secondary period and flourished during the tertiary. Within the class of mammals, the highest order is that of the primates. And the primates are divided, in ascending order, into lemurs, monkeys and hominians. The necessity of classifying the fossils discovered within the last century has led to the distinguishing, within the hominians, a family of *Hominidae*, and within that family an unique genus called *Homo*—Man.

[1] A. Varagnac, *De la Préhistoire au Monde moderne* (Paris, 1954), p. 3 of Introduction.

Within this genus, prehistorians have established a number of varieties, which they are uncertain whether to treat as *species* or as merely *races* belonging to the same species. The view at present prevailing is that the genus Homo comprises, at least at the present day and perhaps also in prehistory, only one species: *Homo sapiens*, or man endowed with reason.

Whereas there are a great many species of monkeys, there is only one species of man, as we know him and despite the number of different races. Such an anomaly in animal nomenclature deserves consideration. It may be taken for certain, from the scientific point of view, that all men are brothers, in the sense that all are of the same genus and species, and all belong to the same *syngameon*, by which is meant that they are all capable of uniting in marriage to produce fertile offspring.

This community of species affords a glimpse of the underlying community of origin. Nor need we attach too great importance to the extensive nomenclature invented by prehistorians during the last half-century. When we come upon such names as the following, which we translate from the Latin, Cape Man, Modjokerto Man, Steinheim Man, Kanam Man, not to mention, as we shall see later, Neanderthal Man and Cro-Magnon Man, there is no sufficient reason for supposing that we are dealing with different species of men. From the moment when we can say with confidence that we are dealing with rational creatures, as proved by their employment of tools and weapons, there are no valid grounds for excluding them from the great human family. And at this point philosophy once more comes to the rescue by justly blaming those scientists who contrast *Homo faber*, the Neanderthal man, with *Homo sapiens*, who is Cro-Magnon man and our direct ancestor.

Philosophy holds—correctly, it must be admitted—that one cannot be *faber*, which means a skilled worker or maker, without intelligence, and that it is the possession of intelligence or reason that automatically entitles one to the designation *sapiens*. *Homo faber* is undoubtedly, as we shall see, a man, and is therefore equally undoubtedly *Homo sapiens* from the philosopher's point of view.

All this will become apparent in our discussion of this problem, brief though we are compelled to be.

THE "ANTHROPIAN" PROBLEM

We have pointed out that there exists today a very clearly defined gap between man and those animals most closely related to him such as the gorilla, the chimpanzee, the orang-utang and the gibbon. But this gap was not always so wide, a fact revealed by two sets of figures. The brain capacity of the present day ape is less than 600 cubic centimetres as against 1,400 or 1,500 for the human brain. This is a considerable difference. But fossils have been found with brain capacities half-way between those of the monkey and of man. Thus, Dubois's Pithecanthropus, discovered in Java, measured 850 cubic centimetres, and Sinanthropus, found in Chu-Ku-Tien about thirty miles south-west of Peking, measured as much as 1,200 cubic centimetres.

We are here faced with the so-called "anthropian problem". At what degree of brain capacity did human "psychism", by which is meant a human mind endowed with intelligence and reason, make its appearance? It is impossible to say. Our only criterion is the presence or absence of tools or weapons. More-over, these implements must derive from human initiative, for the proof of human status is not to be based on the presence of a club, for example, which is not hand-made and has been discarded after use, as appears to have happened in the case of certain recently discovered South African fossil apes known as Australopitheci.

Now it is precisely to the Java Pithecanthropus that it has proved impossible to attribute with certainty any tool or weapon of his own invention. More doubtful is the case of Sinanthropus, in whose vicinity traces of hearths have been found, together with wooden and bone cutting implements fashioned into tools. However, experts disagree over the attribution to Sinanthropus himself of the prolonged acquaintance with fire and employment of tools implied by these discoveries. Strictly speaking, Sinanthropus might have been rather the victim than the inventor of the tool-weapons in question. Some hitherto undiscovered species of man may have hunted Sinanthropus for food. Traces of such a species have perhaps been discovered in other caves than those in which Sinanthropus was found. Nevertheless, it cannot with certainty be maintained that the fossils thus discovered are really of the same age as Sinanthropus. The latter seems to date from at least 500,000 years ago. Was he a man or a mere mindless hominian? So far the question remains unanswered. We shall return to it in the chapter setting out our conclusions.

NEANDERTHAL MAN

We are much better informed when we come to Neanderthal Man, who is in any case much younger than Sinanthropus, Pithecanthropus and his near relative Africanthropus.

This fossil creature takes his name from the Neanderthal valley near Düsseldorf, where the first skull associated with him was found in 1856.

In 1908 three French priests, keen prehistorians, the brothers Amédée and Jean Bouyssonnie and Abbé Louis Bardon, discovered at Corrèze, south-east of Brive, in a village called La Chapelle-aux-Saints, a complete skeleton of the same prehistoric type. Since that date there have been many more discoveries, and we now possess dozens of remains of Neanderthal Man. A thorough study of him was made by Marcellin Boule, who describes him in the following terms which have become classical:

Trunk short and massive, enormous head, with facial portion over-developed in relation to the cerebral portion. Cranial index average. Abnormally flattened skull, huge orbital arches forming a continuous ridge, markedly receding forehead, occiput projecting and vertically compressed. Long, prominent face, with flat, receding cheek-bones, upper maxillaries lacking in canine fossae and shaped like a muzzle; extremely large, round eye-sockets. Very large, projecting nose. Enormous sub-nasal space. Massive lower jaw, chinless, with broad rising branches and truncated angular region. Voluminous dentition, morphology of the hind-molars preserving a number of primitive characteristics. Vertebral column and limb bones presenting many pithecoid features and indicating a bipedal or upright posture inferior to that found in present-day man. Very short legs. Average brain capacity about 1,400 cubic centimetres. Cerebral conformation presenting a large number of primitive characteristics, notably in the great reduction of the frontal lobes and in the general pattern of the circumvolutions.

All later discoveries have confirmed this diagnosis. The extremely wide distribution of the Neanderthal type in Europe, Asia and Africa has been demonstrated. Tentative and obviously problematical reconstructions have popularized this kind of man, with his massive head supported on a small thick-set and bent body, walking always apparently with a stoop, the knees bent and the head stretched backwards. His most striking features are the huge superciliary arches forming a very marked and thick bony ridge at the base of the forehead, the absence of chin, and the kind of bony protuberance at the back of the head. A close scrutiny of the inside of the skull has led to the conjecture that the individuals of this type were above all *visuals*, an eminently suitable attribute for a hunting folk, but endowed with somewhat rudimentary capacities for reflection, reasoning and speech.

It is probable that there were many varieties of Neanderthal Man: we possess specimens from Palestine (about fifteen examples), Ngandong in Java (not far from Pithecanthropus), Broken Hill in Rhodesia, Rabat, Tangier, Siberia, The Cape, etc., etc.

To sum up, the more than a hundred fossil remains which we possess bear witness to the extremely wide distribution of this type, which is missing only from Australia and America.

We have remarked that Neanderthal Man is called *Homo faber* by the scientists, and is thereby distinguished from

Homo sapiens from whom we are descended. Yet there are many reasons for attributing intelligence to *Homo faber*, and consequently for treating him from the philosophical point of view as a true *Homo sapiens*, in other words simply as a man.

The reasons to be adduced are: (1) the brain capacity, which is equal to the average of present day man, (2) the command of tools, which is in no way inferior to that observed among adjacent human varieties, and (3) the cult of the dead, a sure sign of membership of the human family. Neanderthal Man has even been credited with one invention in the proper sense of the word, and that is the chisel, which it is possible to attribute to him, and which makes its appearance in the Mousterian deposits about 60,000 years ago. The later Aurignacian and Magdalenian deposits contribute no more than an improvement on the Neanderthal technique. He is also credited with working in bone. Indeed, in certain Neanderthal deposits heaps of bones have been found carefully arranged according to length, a sure indication that they were intended to be put to industrial use.

It is quite possible that Neanderthal Man became intermixed, through marriages which proved fruitful, with various branches of the true *Homo sapiens*, although no proof is forthcoming. What is certain is that this variety of man disappeared, never to return.

Nevertheless, his long survival raises in an acute fashion the twofold problem of *monophyletism* versus *polyphyletism* on the one hand, and on the other of *monogenism* versus *polygenism*.

Here we are confronted with one of the most delicate problems in connection with human origins.

In our closing chapters we shall have occasion to emphasize that the Bible, and subsequently the Church, are plainly *monophyletist* and *monogenist*; and we shall quote conclusive evidence in proof.

For the present we discuss the question from the strictly scientific point of view. What then is the question at issue?

MONOGENISM AND POLYGENISM

Monogenism necessarily implies monophyletism. But the converse is not true, since one may be a monophyletist and a polygenist at the same time.

The problem is whether man (1) derives from a single or from several animal stocks, and (2) whether, assuming the one parent stock, the course of evolution from it leading up to him has been "fan-wise", i.e. in several simultaneous directions, or on the contrary has proceeded from a single human pair from which the entire species is derived.

While admitting the unity of the human species, scientists, who confine their attention to present day man to the exclusion of all fossil men, are almost unanimously agreed that he comes from *one single stock*, *one stem*, or what they call one *phylum*. In this sense they are monophyletists. If we allow, generally speaking, polyphyletism for the simiidae, who are nevertheless so closely related to the hominians, it is difficult to derive the hominians from a number of evolutionary stems.

For this reason Dr. Vallois was able to write: "It is absolutely impossible to establish between the various genera of anthropoids that systematic parallelism which lies at the very base of all polyphyletic theories."

It follows that the descent of man is a unique phenomenon. From the point where his ancestors separated from the neighbouring branches of the evolutionary tree, they suffered no further division. This, however, is no presumption in favour of either monogenism or polygenism. It is indeed possible that several human pairs in different countries might have sprung from the same stock, with the result that the men of today, and *a fortiori* the fossil men, could have derived from different human ancestors. In other words, if we agree that Adam and Eve were the names of the first man and woman, it need not follow that all men are descended from Adam and Eve. In that case, we must attribute a *collective*, and not an *individual* significance to those names. Adam would then designate a *plurality* of men endowed by God with a human soul, and similarly Eve would represent a *plurality of women.*

We shall see that this interpretation has been flatly rejected by the Church.

It must in fairness be said that scientists left to themselves have not been so categorical, and that their inclination seems to be towards polygenism rather than monogenism.

We must now examine the reasons they give for this opinion.

In the first place, the general laws of the differentiation of species, so far as they may be understood from the study of animal evolution in general, seem to show that changes occur "fan-wise" rather than in a single sample; that is to say that new forms must have appeared everywhere at once.

In the second place, the appearance of man in the form of a unique pair would seem to provide too narrow a basis for the development of the human species. In the third place, the Adam of theology must have been born fully adult, a proposition which is meaningless to contemporary science.

We propose to show that these reasons are inconclusive from the scientific, and inadmissible from the theological point of view.

Let us confine ourselves to monogenism, since nothing obliges us to abandon it. We need only allow the first human pair a considerable degree of plasticity (than which nothing could be more natural) to see that all the varieties of man, both fossil and living, may spring from them alone. Consequently, if Sinanthropus is really a man, he is an extinct branch of the family of Adam. The same is true of Neanderthal Man and of all the races of man hitherto enumerated or awaiting discovery by future excavations.

In our final chapter we shall return to this vitally important point.

It remains to consider the hypotheses advanced by science to account for the origin of the first man. We have placed his appearance in the Chellean period at a date of 600,000 or at the lowest between 400,000 and 500,000 B.C. The question asked by the prehistorians concerns the origins of his body.

They are willing to grant that the problem of the origin of the soul lies beyond their reach. It is a question pertaining to philosophy and theology. As for man's body, science contends that it was the result of evolution, though up to the present it remains no more than a "working hypothesis". It has not been proved, and is probably incapable of proof. But it seems an indispensable hypothesis, given the obvious fact of development apparent in all living forms which palaeontology has so far discovered and is continuing to bring to light.

Nothing in theology, no more than in philosophy, is opposed to the acceptance of this continuous evolutionary process.

We shall now review the current speculations of prehistory and palaeontology on the remote origins of mankind.

The topicality of this problem is shown by the visit to the United States at the beginning of 1956 of Dr Johannes Hurzeler, a Swiss palaeontologist from Basle University, for the purpose of exhibiting to a meeting of scientists at the Wenner-Gren Foundation of Anthropological Research the jawbone of an Orepithecus which betrayed human rather than anthropoid features.

Now this jawbone had been discovered in Tuscany in an Upper Miocene stratum at least ten million years older than the oldest human fossils. The Swiss scientist's claims were discussed in the leading New York newspapers. Evolutionists and anti-evolutionists rushed into the fray. With amusement we recall the unfortunate episode of the Piltdown skull, which in 1953 was found to be a fake. Nevertheless the experts were and remain in disagreement. Can one seriously rank Oreopithecus as an ancestor of man? First of all what is Oreopithecus? This fossil has been known since 1872, and was described by the French palaeontologist Paul Gervais (1816–79), who classified it as a prehistoric ape. At that time it was described as follows: "A genus of fossil ape whose lower jawbone, found in Tuscany in the Upper Miocene, presents the characteristics of the cynocephalus, the gibbon and the anthropoid ape." The new specimen brought forward by Dr Hurzeler seemed to be closer to man than to the ape in certain features. Dr Hurzeler claimed that it was a "mannikin" of very great antiquity from the point of view of its bodily structure. The human features he found in it were the following: vertical forehead descending in a straight line towards the teeth; narrow face; well-developed brain.

In order to understand the importance of this description we must recall what happened in the case of the genealogy of the horse. The history of the Equidae is a favourite theme of palaeontologists. It is, in effect, the typical example of what is called *orthoselective orthogenesis*, that is, the evolution in one definite direction of several characteristics which recur with accumulating modifications throughout the length of the series.

These characteristics are: increase in height, elongation of the face, expansion of the brain, adaptation of the foot by a reduction in the number of toes until the hoof stage is reached, adaptation of the teeth to a vegetable diet, elongation of the neck and strengthening of the back.

It has proved possible to reconstruct most of the stages in this evolution of the horse. We begin sixty million years ago with *Eohippus* and *Hyracotherium*. At this stage the ancestral horse is no bigger than a fox terrier. Later on, the series is continued by *Orohippus*. *Epihippus* makes its appearance in the middle Eocene epoch. In the Oligocene we come to *Mesohippus*, the size of an adult greyhound. Later still, *Miohippus* is the size of a sheep. *Parahippus*, in the lower Miocene, is slightly larger. Soon afterwards, the Equidae increase in numbers, and we find *Desmatippus*, *Merychippus* and *Protohippus*. At this point there is a side-branch terminating in *Hipparion*, which vanishes leaving no descendants.

Pliohippus, still a member of the same *phylum*, reaches the size of a pony, and has only one toe left of the original five. Finally, in the Pliocene, we come to *Plesippus*, who is now the size of a horse, of which, in the quaternary epoch, our genus *Equus* is a direct descendant.

It is some such genealogical tree that the palaeontologists would like to discover for man. Accordingly they are not surprised at the diminutive stature of the remote ancestor. Some scientists look for this ancestor not to Oreopithecus but to a small creature of the size of a kitten called a *tarsier* (*Tarsius spectrum*). This creature has enormous eyes, and a brain which relates it to the lower apes.

In 1918 the British anatomist F. Wood Jones argued that man was of tarsioid rather than of anthropoid descent. In his opinion, man's ancestors must have been small but exceedingly active animals, already provided with long legs, small jaws with no prominent teeth, and broad skulls. The theories of Wood Jones met with strong opposition, but a famous American palaeontologist, H. Fairfield Osborne, came near to them in his opinion that the ancestors of man should be sought for in the line of animals furnished with pre-human legs. In his own words: "I predict that as far back as the upper Oligocene we shall come upon 'pre-men', and that these creatures will be found to have 'pre-human' limbs."

So far, however, we are dealing only with a prediction. In actual fact, the theories concerning the descent of man can be reduced to three.

According to the first theory, a common ancestor of the anthropoid apes and of man left descendants which diverged since the beginning of the Pliocene epoch, about eight million years ago. This ancestor must have been an ape with both simian and human characteristics. He can be assigned a place near to Parapithecus and Propliopithecus. Among his simian descendants must be placed the famous Proconsul, the recently discovered African fossil ape, after him Dryopithecus, and last the various extant higher apes such as the chimpanzee, the gorilla and the orang-utang.

The second theory goes much further back in time, for it assumes that the common ancestor flourished at the height of the Oligocene, at least forty million years ago. This ancestor shared the characteristics of the first primates, the apes and the anthropoids. It is in this line of descent that Oreopithecus should be placed. Hitherto, however, the latter has been regarded as an offshoot without descendants, somewhat like Hipparion in the genealogy of the horse. Dr Hurzeler, on the contrary, wishes to regard him as a link in the line of human descent. This line of descent may therefore be assumed to start from Parapithecus, who existed at the beginning of the Oligocene, and was the ancestor of two divergent branches at the end of the Oligocene. One of these branches led through Propliopithecus to Proconsul, Dryopithecus and the great apes of the present day. But it also led to Pliopithecus, and from him to the gibbon, another kind of ape. Finally, in its most interesting line, which according to Hurzeler passed through Oreopithecus, it led to the South African Australopithecus (perhaps a divergent type with no descendants), then to the prehominians and finally to man and his varieties, Neanderthal Man and Cro-Magnon Man, himself barely distinguishable from Grimaldi Man and Chancelade Man.

Lastly, a third theory goes even further back in time, and claims to identify man's ancestor in a creature of very small stature who lived in the Eocene, like the ancestor of the horse, between forty-five and fifty million years further back. This ancestor was a tarsier.

This multiplicity of opinions suffices to prove that much light still remains to be thrown on this extremely complicated problem.

In a survey of current controversy published in *The Scientific American* for June 1956, an expert, Loren C. Eiseley, makes the following very sensible remarks:

> For the successful reconstruction of the evolution of the horse in the Tertiary Period, palaeontologists had thousands of fossil bones to study. Primatologists may therefore be forgiven their fumblings over great gaps of millions of years from which we do not possess a single complete monkey skeleton, let alone the skeleton of a human forerunner. For the whole Tertiary Period, which involves something like 60 to 80 million years, we have to read the story of primate evolution from a few handfuls of broken bones and teeth. Those fossils, moreover,

are from places thousands of miles apart on the Old World land mass.

In point of fact the tarsier is distributed over the Malay Archipelago and the Philippines, whereas Parapithecus was discovered at Fayum in Egypt, while Oreopithecus was found, as we have seen, in Tuscany.

The same writer concludes with the following wise observation:

> To continue our writing of the story of human evolution we are totally dependent upon finding additional fossils. Until further discoveries accumulate, each student will perhaps inevitably read a little of his own temperament into the record. . . . It is as though we stood at the heart of a maze and no longer remembered how we had come there.

So far, therefore, we cannot speak of an undisputed line of descent from animal to man. Everything written on the subject must, pending further enquiry, be treated more or less as an "historical novel". Nearly a century ago Ernest Renan wrote of our little "conjectural sciences". It was to history properly so called that his words referred. What are we to call the hypotheses of palaeontology regarding the origins of man?

CHAPTER IV

THE ORIGINS OF MAN ACCORDING TO THE BIBLE AND THE TEACHING OF THE CHURCH

A HIGHER SOURCE OF INFORMATION

So far we have consulted three sources of information on the origins of man: mythology, philosophy and science. The answers they supply cannot all be treated on the same footing. Mythology, while witnessing to the instinctive and passionate interest taken by mankind in this kind of problem, has been unable to do more than ask questions to which, for the most part if not always, it has provided replies which are inadequate and puerile, and in any case lacking any rational basis. Philosophy, in its attack on the same problems, has constructed such a variety of systems that we remain in perplexity as to which we should prefer. Indeed, many have thought that the multiplicity of theories was bound to lead to complete scepticism. Lastly the sciences of astronomy, palaeontology and prehistory have succeeded in providing us with definite facts. Today we know more or less what status in space and time we are to assign to the earth and its inhabitants. The majority of scientists now agree that the broad fact of evolution ending in man as its latest product no longer admits of discussion, although it is not at present possible to trace with accuracy, let alone with certainty, the genealogical tree from which we are sprung.

Is this the utmost we can hope to know of our origins? Have we no other source of information? And if there is some other source, what is its worth and what light can it throw?

Such is the question to which we shall address ourselves in what is undoubtedly the most important chapter in this little book.

To the question as put we return the firm reply: yes, we have another source of information, a source which for us bears a name of high prestige—*divine revelation.* The volumes of the first part of this series have all been devoted to proving the existence of this source.

Here then we shall take for proved the existence of divine revelation. We shall also assume an acquaintance with the two main sources of this revelation, the Bible and Tradition, and the manner in which they are offered, explained and vouched for to us, by the teaching of the Church. In conclusion, we shall maintain that theology, which is the science of the facts of revelation and of the conclusions to be drawn from it, is for us a source of information surpassing all others in depth and certainty, provided only that it confines itself scrupulously and strictly within the limits which are appropriate to it and are those desired by God.

CONCORDISM AND ITS ILLUSIONS

For so long as neither astronomy nor physics had anything definite to say about the world and man, it was inevitable that the theologians should put their faith in what they conceived to be the teaching of the Bible on this subject. That the earth was stationary in the centre of the universe seemed to them to be established not only by sense perception but by holy Writ. It was further agreed that the word of God confirmed what all the philosophers and scientists since the days of Greece had maintained, that the world was composed of four elements.

The first conflict between science and theology was the trial of Galileo. It is now universally recognized that in this affair the theologians exceeded their functions, and through a mistaken interpretation of the Bible made an unfortunate intrusion into the field of science.

More recently, when geology was beginning to construct a chronology of the earth's strata, the reaction of the theologians was twofold. Some, and those the least well informed, expressed doubts concerning the calculations of the scientists and the date assigned by them to the creation. They clung tenaciously to the year 4004 B.C. which we have already encountered in the opening lines of Bossuet's *Discours sur l'histoire universelle*. Others adopted the more cautious line of attempting to establish between the scientific and the biblical data a hitherto unnoticed but thereby all the more striking concordance. This process is known as "concordism". It may be said to go back to Georges Cuvier, but was greatly extended after his time. The scientists spoke of "geological epochs", and behold! all that was required was to give the widest possible interpretation to the "days" spoken of in the Bible. These "days" became "epochs". Biblical passages were quoted in which the word Yom, which means a day, was used to signify a period of indefinite duration (Exodus 10. 6; Leviticus 7. 35, 36, etc.). A remark frequently made was that the saying in Genesis 1. 3 "Be light made" carried a remarkable application to the nebular hypothesis of Laplace, so that the creation of the sun and moon on the fourth "day", following the creation of the plants on the third, corresponded in a remarkable manner to the actual emergence of the sun and moon after the dissipation of the exceedingly dense vapours of the primitive atmosphere. For a long time these explanations appeared both convincing and praiseworthy. They were taught in the seminaries, and met with universal acceptance.

At length, however, it became clear that these explanations needed revising to keep pace with the progress of science. New discoveries compelled the scientists to repudiate their previous conclusions: the theologians found themselves lagging in the rear. Finally they awoke to their true position, which owing to the incessant changes in the findings of science was becoming not only uncomfortable but frankly ridiculous.

The clearest-sighted pointed out the mistake that had been made, to which attention had already been called by St Augustine in his *De Genesi ad litteram*, and which consisted in reading the Bible as if it were a "book of science" instead of a "book of salvation". The function of the Bible is not to tell us what our intelligence can find out by its own resources, but to show us the way which leads to eternal happiness, a way which it is not in the power of either science or philosophy to open or reveal to us.

Thenceforth concordism was superseded. And this is one of the most important advances made by exegesis, under the pressure of scientific research itself, during the last half century. Today it is readily accepted that the Bible is not to be consulted as if it were a scientific treatise, and that such seemingly scientific facts as are to be found in it have no other value than to inform us of the ideas current at the different times at which the books composing it were written.

We shall now make direct application of this principle to a re-reading of the first chapters of Genesis, the chief text dealing with the origins of man and the world.

THE TWO NARRATIVES OF GENESIS

The long labours of the exegetes, finally ratified by the Church in a Letter of the Biblical Commission dated January 16th, 1948, and more particularly in the Encyclical *Humani generis* dated August 12th, 1950, to which we shall have frequent occasion to refer, ended in a very important preliminary finding, to the effect that the opening chapters of Genesis contain two different narratives which, while converging on the same essential truths, set out these truths in very different ways, each of which requires to be studied separately.

Of these two narratives it is natural that one should be older than the other, for it is inconceivable that both should come from the same date and pen.

The older of these narratives is not that which comes first in Genesis as we have it, but that which begins at verse 4 of

Chapter 2. It has been given the name of the "patriarchal" narrative *par excellence*, because it records a tradition derived from the patriarchs. It is more concrete, more earthy so to speak. Its background is the life of the desert, and its authorship is attributed to Moses, the great legislator of the Hebrew people, though it did not receive its final shape until the tenth century B.C.

The second narrative is in a grander style. It soars aloft and surveys from on high the details of the creation. It is younger in age, and has been given the title of the "priestly" narrative. It is more abstract than its "patriarchal" predecessor. Its background is Babylonia, where it aims at installing the faith of God's chosen people. It was probably composed during the Exile, in the sixth century B.C. and long after the time of Moses.

For our purposes it is a most remarkable and instructive circumstance that the committee of priests (for we are probably not dealing with one single author, whose work could not have supplanted a whole popular tradition) which brought out, if we may use the term, a revised and completed edition of Genesis, left untouched the version of Moses, in full awareness of the differences between the two. The reason was, that for the new editors the old version was sacred; apart from the fact that its teaching was identical with that prevailing among contemporary enlightened Jews. Moreover, it is inconceivable that the "priestly" teaching made a sudden appearance: it also was a "tradition", and no less patriarchal than the Mosaic. But it was probably with a view to distinguishing more clearly between the doctrine of God's people and all foreign doctrines that, when Genesis came to be "re-edited", the "priestly" narrative was given pride of place.

For the profitable study of these two narratives it is necessary to bear constantly in mind the exhortation of Pope Pius XII in his Encyclical *Divino afflante* of September 30th, 1947: "It is absolutely necessary for the interpreter to go back in spirit to those remote centuries of the East, and make proper use of the aids afforded by history, archaeology, ethnology and other sciences, in order to discover what literary forms the writers of that early age intended to use, and did in fact employ."

This conception of "literary forms" is by now fully established, and is essential to all exegesis.

All this in no way detracts from the "inspiration" exhibited from beginning to end of Holy Writ.[1]

Here we must be content to summarize the dogma as follows: It is God who is the chief author of Holy Writ. The writers of the books are God's instruments; but they are free agents because they are men, and God has an absolute respect for human freedom, of which he is the author. Accordingly God actuates their will, and sheds his divine light on their human intelligence, so that they may appreciate the spiritual worth of the persons and things of which they write. He helps them, at least negatively, in the act of writing, so that no doctrinal error may creep in. This divine action interpenetrates the human activity which is subordinate to it in the composition of the Scriptures, to the extent that any statement made by an author of the sacred books is equally a statement made by God. But the Word of God is spoken in the accents of the human voice. As has been well said by Jean Guitton, "God is careful to do nothing beyond what it is indispensable for him to do. He delegates to free creatures all of his powers which are capable of being delegated."

It is for this reason that, for the understanding and interpretation of the Word of God, attention must be paid to the "literary style" employed by the human writer. It follows that the sacred Book deserves to be studied with the same care as is devoted by critics to a profane book.

We shall now attempt a brief study of this kind of the two creation stories contained in Genesis.

THE PATRIARCHAL NARRATIVE

We must first read the text with the profoundest reverence,

---

[1] The dogma of inspiration will be subjected to careful examination in the present series in the volumes dealing with the Bible.

as constituting the oldest written document known to us concerning the origins of man.

So were heaven and earth made; heaven and earth, alike of
God's fashioning. But no woodland shrub had yet grown, no
wild plant yet sprung up; the Lord God had not yet sent rain
upon the ground, that still had no human toil to cultivate it;
there was only spring-water which came up from the earth,
and watered its whole surface. And now, from the clay of the
ground, the Lord God formed man, breathed into his nostrils
the breath of life, and made man a living soul. Already he had
planted a garden of delight, in which he now placed the man
he had formed. Here, at the bidding of the Lord God, the soil
produced all such trees as charm the eye and satisfy the taste;
and here, in the middle of the garden, grew the tree of life,
and the tree which brings knowledge of good and evil. The
garden was watered by a river; it came out from the place called
the place of Delight, and went on to divide into four branches.
One is called Phison; it is the river which surrounds all the
country of Hevilath, a gold-producing country; no gold is
better; bdellium is found there too, and the onyx-stone. The
second river is called Gehon, and is the river which surrounds
the whole country of Ethiopia. The third river, which flows past
the Assyrians, is called Tigris, and the fourth is the river
Euphrates. So the Lord God took the man and put him in his
garden of delight, to cultivate and tend it. And this was the
command which the Lord God gave the man, Thou mayest
eat thy fill of all the trees in the garden except the tree which
brings knowledge of good and evil; if ever thou eatest of this,
thy doom is death.

But the Lord God said, It is not well that man should be
without companionship; I will give him a mate of his own
kind. And now, from the clay of the ground, all the wild beasts
and all that flies through the air were ready fashioned, and the
Lord God brought them to Adam, to see what he would call
them; the name Adam gave to each living creature is its name
still. Thus Adam gave names to all the cattle, and all that flies
in the air, and all the wild beasts; and still Adam had no mate
of his own kind. So the Lord God made Adam fall into a deep
sleep, and, while he slept, took away one of his ribs, and filled

its place with flesh. This rib, which he had taken out of Adam, the Lord God formed into a woman; and when he brought her to Adam, Adam said, Here, at last, is bone that comes from mine, flesh that comes from mine; it shall be called Woman, this thing that was taken out of Man. That is why a man is destined to leave father and mother, and cling to his wife instead, so that the two become one flesh. Both went naked, Adam and his wife, and thought it no shame. (Genesis 2. 4–25.)

In this artless and obviously primitive story certain features are conspicuous. In the first place, we are undoubtedly dealing with the creation of the universe. When the Bible speaks of "heaven and earth" it is referring to the whole universe. In the second place, the earth was to begin with a desert, the soil is naked, dry and desolate. Here especially does this version of the story betray the influence of the desert through which the Hebrews passed in the time of Moses. It is as a desert that the world is here represented, before the creation of man. God then creates water and man, without whom no agriculture is possible. As seen through the eyes of Moses there is no sign of a type of man ignorant of agriculture, and living in the forest by hunting and fruit-gathering.

According to Moses, God made a garden in which to place man. This garden is Eden. Man's task is to keep it and *cultivate* it. To help him, God creates the domestic animals, and brings them to the man to be named. Note that the creation of the animals includes only the "wild beasts" and "all that flies through the air": no mention is made of fish or of forest animals.

In this archaic story our particular attention is directed to the creation of man, which is told partly in the form of a myth, overlaid, that is, with anthropomorphic and poetic images.

In the course of time man had acquired the art of pottery, which had grown, we may say, to be one of the commonest forms of human industry. Accordingly Moses in his narrative represents God in the guise of a potter who takes some clay and moulds it to the shape desired. It is, however, made quite clear that this process applies only to man's body: it is God himself who imparts a soul to this body by breathing into its nostrils the breath of life. Moreover, since there is no mention of this breath of life in the creation of the animals, we are intended to recognize a clear-cut distinction between the human and the animal soul. This distinction becomes even more apparent when we read how the man, in his need of a helpmeet to cheer his loneliness, cannot find one suitable among the animals upon whom he is bestowing names. It follows that he is of an entirely different nature.

In its turn the creation of woman assumes a poetical and mythical form. It takes place in an atmosphere of mystery, indicated by the use of the term "sleep". The first man had no knowledge of what God was preparing for him as he lay asleep. For him, the woman is drawn "from a rib", which perhaps bears some such meaning as "from man's desire", symbolized by the rib's proximity to the heart. In any case, the man easily recognizes in the woman a being of flesh and bone like himself, endowed with a similar kind of life, superior to that of the animals. He calls her *ischa*, the feminine of *isch*, thereby indicating woman's submission with respect to man. Finally, the marriage is described in splendid words, which Christ repeated in all their original purity. The love which presides over marriage is superior to any other love. A man will leave his father and mother to cling to his wife, and their union will be so close that "the two become one flesh".

In this first period their nakedness does not trouble them, since both are in a state of perfect moral equilibrium.

It is impossible not to recognize the majestic splendour of such a narrative. When, in our last chapter, we come to compare it with its nearest, Babylonian, parallels, we shall have no difficulty in demonstrating its divine and overwhelming superiority.

But we must now return to the second narrative, which in Genesis precedes that which we have discussed above.

PROBABLE REASONS FOR THE SECOND VERSION

The reasons which led to a new version of the primitive

story of the Creation of the world and man by God may be surmised to be approximately the following. The first narrative no longer corresponded with the increase which had come about in men's knowledge of the world. Israel had come into contact with her neighbours. As we have seen in our second chapter, the sixth century B.C. witnessed the adoption in every quarter of a more rational explanation of the universe. Chiefly in Greece, but also in India, the need was felt for a fundamental revision of the ancient mythologies. It was the time when the Jews were carried off to captivity in Babylonia. Obviously we cannot now trace the influences at work in the revised narrative. Some priest was inspired to re-handle the primitive stories of the chosen people. We have pointed out that this priest could hardly have worked alone and on his own authority. This does not imply the existence of an "editorial board": it is more natural to imagine a team engaged in reflection, revision and preparation. And it was at this point that the new narrative took shape. At the same time, the second editor, while presenting everything in a new light, did not interfere with the old story. The reason, no doubt, was that he recognized its inspired character. While, however, giving it a new form, he discreetly conveyed its primitive and archaic quality. He also avoids its most elementary anthropomorphisms. We are not, of course, to look in this second version, any more than in the first, for the slightest "scientific" purpose in our own sense of the term. Never again shall we repeat the words of Lacordaire, who in 1848 said of the book of Genesis, the whole of which he attributed to Moses alone: "Fifteen centuries before the Christian era Moses was in possession of scientific knowledge which it took three thousand years to bring to light."

Our own view is that neither Moses, nor the anonymous sixth-century editor of his work had any concern whatever with science. Neither was it the purpose of God, the author of Holy Writ, to instruct us in science any more than in philosophy. But the three branches of knowledge—science, philosophy and theology—while employing different methods and providing complementary facts, should converge without merging.

Let us now examine the "priestly" narrative of creation, as it was composed in the sixth century B.C.

THE PRIESTLY NARRATIVE

God, at the beginning of time, created heaven and earth. Earth was still an empty waste, and darkness hung over the deep; but already, over its waters, brooded the Spirit of God. Then God said, Let there be light; and the light began. God saw the light, and found it good, and he divided the spheres of light and darkness; the light he called Day, and the darkness Night. So evening came, and morning, and one day passed. God said, too, Let a solid vault arise amid the waters, to keep these waters apart from those; a vault by which God would separate the waters which were beneath it from the waters above it; and so it was done. This vault God called the sky. So evening came, and morning, and a second day passed.

And now God said, Let the waters below the vault collect in one place to make dry land appear. And so it was done; the dry land God called Earth, and the water, where it had collected, he called the Sea. All this God saw, and found it good. Let the earth, he said, yield grasses that grow and seed; fruit-trees too, each giving fruit of its own kind, and so propagating itself on earth. And so it was done; the earth yielded grasses that grew and seeded, each according to its kind, and trees that bore fruit, each with the power to propagate its own kind. And God saw it, and found it good. So evening came, and morning, and a third day passed.

Next, God said, Let there be luminaries in the vault of the sky, to divide the spheres of day and night; let them give portents, and be the measures of time, to mark out the day and the year; let them shine in the sky's vault, and shed light on the earth. And so it was done.

God made the two great luminaries, the greater of them to command the day, and the lesser to command the night; then he made the stars. All these he put in the vault of the sky, to shed their light on the earth, to control day and night, and divide the spheres of light and darkness. And God saw it, and found it good. So evening came, and morning, and a fourth day passed.

After this, God said, Let the waters produce moving things that have life in them, and winged things that fly above the earth under the sky's vault. Thus God created the huge sea-beasts, and all the different kinds of life and movement that spring from the waters, and all the different kinds of flying things; and God saw it, and found it good. He pronounced his blessing on them, Increase and multiply, and fill the waters of the sea; and let there be abundance of flying things on the earth. So evening came, and morning, and a fifth day passed. God said, too, Let the land yield all different kinds of living things, cattle and creeping things and wild beasts of every sort; and so it was done. God made every sort of wild beast, and all the different kinds of cattle and of creeping things; and God saw it, and found it good.

And God said, Let us make man, wearing our own image and likeness; let us put him in command of the fishes in the sea, and all that flies through the air, and the cattle, and the whole earth, and all the creeping things that move on earth. So God made man in his own image, made him in the image of God. Man and woman both, he created them. And God pronounced his blessing on them, Increase and multiply and fill the earth, and make it yours; take command of the fishes in the sea, and all that flies through the air, and all the living things that move on the earth. Here are all the herbs, God told them, that seed on earth, and all the trees, that carry in them the seeds of their own life, to be your food; food for all the beasts on the earth, and all that flies in the air, all that creeps along the ground; here all that lives shall find its nourishment. And so it was done. And God saw all that he had made, and found it very good. So evening came, and morning, and a sixth day passed.

Thus heaven and earth and all the furniture of them were completed. By the seventh day, God had come to an end of making, and rested, on the seventh day, with his whole task accomplished. That is why God gave the seventh day his blessing, and hallowed it, because it was the day on which his divine activity of creation finished. So were heaven and earth made; heaven and earth, alike of God's fashioning. (Genesis 1. 1–2. 5.)

A SHORT COMMENTARY

To begin with, let us consider these last words. They claim that this is indeed the history of heaven and earth, that is, of the creation of the whole universe. In the context it is neither necessary nor even possible to take the word history in its scientific sense. History is compiled from documents: here there were no documents. History follows a chronological order: here there is indeed a chronological order, but it is artificial.

We are dealing, then, with a "popular" history, which has the clearly defined aim of instructing a people chosen by God in the essential truths concerning the origins of the universe and of man himself.

These stories, in the words of the Biblical Commission's previously quoted letter of January 16th, 1948, "convey in simple and figurative language adapted to the intelligence of a less fully developed community the fundamental truths implied in the scheme of salvation, together with a popular account of the origins of mankind and of the chosen people".

What we have called the "priestly" narrative in no respect contradicts the "patriarchal" narrative. It is, however, more sparing in anthropomorphisms. It is grander, fuller, and more philosophical. It omits certain details, notably the creation of the woman from the rib of the man. In the new version man and woman are created together and to the same design. The three phrases describing their creation may be regarded as a kind of sacred song:

> So God made man in his own image,
> Made him in the image of God.
> Man and woman both, he created them.

The triple repetition reminds us of a hymn, and the solemn tone of the words "Let us make man wearing our own image" (note the royal "us") contributes to the impression of majesty.

The deity is here conceived of in the most spiritual terms. God has only to command, and all things obey his word. It is he who creates, he who names, he who blesses and approves. On each occasion he pronounces that everything is "good", and on the last he even sees that everything is "very good". There is none of the dualism which we find in the parallel Persian narrative. There is no hint of a power of evil withstanding the Creator. We can discover not the slightest opposition to his sovereign will.

The teaching to be found in this incomparable cosmogony is the following:

In the first place, a strict *monotheism*. All the objects worshipped by the neighbouring peoples, the sun, the moon, the animals, the plants, etc., are here presented as mere creatures. There is no possibility of confusion. It is the one true God who is the author of all things. No worship is to be offered to anything besides him.

In the second place, there is no pre-existing matter. The world is created from the void, that is, *ex nihilo*, nor is the void to be understood as a kind of matter out of which something can be made.

In the third place, the *dignity of man* stands out splendidly from the whole narrative. This creation of mankind is the result of a kind of special deliberation. Man is declared to be made to the image and likeness of God, a conception which was to provide future theologians and mystics with inexhaustible food for meditation, contemplation and commentary. We need only recall the splendid pages of Bossuet in the fourth week of his *Elévations sur les mystères*, particularly the sixth meditation.

In the fourth place, Genesis explicitly confers upon man *dominion* over all the inferior creatures.

In the fifth place, human marriage is extolled as constituting an intimate union, not only of a physical but above all of a moral kind. Husband and wife become as it were "a single being". What stronger words could be found to express the intimacy which should obtain between them? Later on, Jesus was to declare that, according to the original intention of the creator, this union was to be indissoluble, which it has become again through him. The objects of marriage are also clearly indicated: they are, in the order in which they are stated, mutual help, the increase of the human race, profitable and civilizing labour.

Lastly, Genesis argues powerfully for the *original goodness* of all things. The words "And God saw it and found it good" recur like a refrain after each act of creation. And at the end of the six days we are told once more: "And God saw all that he had made, and found it very good" (1. 31).

THE ORIGIN OF EVIL

At the same time Genesis does not ignore the existence of evil. The story of its origin connects it with what we call original sin. By this term we mean on the one hand the *personal* sin of Adam and Eve, and on the other hand the sin transmitted to all their descendants. This latter category of sin assumes an exceptional importance in Christian theology. Without original sin there would be no need for universal redemption, and the incarnation of the Son of God would not have the same purpose, which is the salvation of fallen man. The new Adam has but to take up the original heritage of the first Adam. The whole of Christianity is as it were inverted.

It is above all in St Paul that we find a perfect exposition of these truths.

To begin with, it is remarkable that the account given in Genesis of the disobedience of Adam and Eve has no equivalent in the pagan traditions. We find only remote analogies in certain Babylonian and Egyptian myths.

The Babylonian hero Gilgamesh sets out in search of the "plant of life" (which reminds us of the "tree of life"), and enters a luxuriant garden after slaying the divine monster which guards its entrance. There he secures the "plant", but a serpent robs him of the spoils.

In connection with the fall of man, all that we can find to

quote is the Egyptian myth of Adapa. In an outburst of ungovernable rage, Adapa has broken the wings of the wind god. He is, however, pardoned by the lord of the gods. All this is infinitely remote from the story in Genesis. It is polytheistic in content. Sin is something external and involuntary: there is no conception of interior sin.

Let us then go on to the third chapter of Genesis, which the sixth-century "priestly narrative" declined to revise in any respect.

The agent of the temptation is the serpent, in which mythical figure the whole of biblical tradition is agreed in recognizing Satan. In the words of the Book of Wisdom: "By the envy of the devil, death came into the world" (2. 24). In the Gospel according to St John, Jesus declares that Satan was "a murderer from the beginning".

The Apocalypse is even more explicit. After describing the great battle of the angels, the author says: "The great dragon, the serpent of the primal age, was flung down to earth; he whom we call the devil, or Satan, the whole world's seducer" (Apoc. 12. 9).

The serpent then, according to Genesis, addresses himself first to the woman, who is the weaker part of humanity but is destined to bring to fruition the work of the tempter. The devil is a master of cunning. He first asks a simple question, as if prompted by natural curiosity. Then follows the emphatic denial: "No, you shall not die the death!" Finally comes the treacherous and monstrous insinuation that God is jealous lest man, by knowing good and evil, becomes like God. By this means the devil arouses the woman's desire. On the other hand, her senses are attracted by the forbidden fruit. She longs to taste it. She gives it to her husband to eat. The sin is committed. At once the first human pair find themselves in a state of moral disequilibrium such as they have not yet known. Adam and Eve are ashamed of their nakedness. Punishment is swift to follow. God questions them closely. From the whole story as told in Genesis it is clear that some catastrophe of the utmost gravity has befallen them. It is undeniable that this narrative might pass ostensibly for a "fairy-tale" resembling the Babylonian myths. One thing is certain, that Adam and Eve resisted God's commands, formally disobeyed them, and were punished for their contumacy by the complete withdrawal of those *supernatural* and *preternatural* gifts with which they had originally been endowed. The serpent is cursed by God, and told that he will one day be finally crushed by "the offspring of the woman". But man had forfeited the divine companionship. Henceforth he is afraid of God. He is ashamed of his "nakedness". The tree of life is forbidden to man, symbolizing the loss of physical immortality, which was a preternatural gift, to be recovered only in the person of the Blessed Virgin Mary, who is exempt from original sin. Henceforth man is given over to death. In the tremendous words of St Paul: "It was through one man that guilt came into the world; and, since death came owing to guilt, death was handed on to all mankind by one man. . . . Grace has been more amply bestowed than ever; that so, where guilt held its reign of death, justifying grace should reign instead, to bring us eternal life through Jesus Christ our Lord" (Rom. 5. 12, 21).

But original sin is to be punished not only by death, but by all the suffering attendant upon human life. Genesis paints a striking picture of the trials which are man's portion, trials which prefigure the passion and cross of our Saviour:

> To the woman he said, Many are the pangs, many are the throes I will give thee to endure; with pangs thou shalt give birth to children, and thou shalt be subject to thy husband; he shall be thy lord. And to Adam he said, Thou hast listened to thy wife's counsel, and hast eaten the fruit I forbade thee to eat; and now through thy act, the ground is under a curse. All the days of thy life thou shalt win food from it with toil; thorns and thistles it shall yield thee, this ground from which thou dost win thy food. Still thou shalt earn thy bread with the sweat of thy brow, until thou goest back into the ground from which thou wast taken; dust thou art, and unto dust thou shalt return (Genesis 3. 16–19).

It is undeniable that beneath this vivid imagery lie lessons of the profoundest importance.

Christian theology has in fact derived from them the following doctrines: Man was created in a state of innocence and perfection. A number of "gifts" were added to his natural properties and faculties. In the first place there was *grace*, expressed in the "divine intimacy", a real "participation in the divine life" which is thereafter only to be found, apart from Jesus, in the Blessed Virgin Mary who is "full of grace". In the second place there were the preternatural gifts of *integrity*, or moral equilibrium (absence of tendency towards evil), *intellectual equilibrium* (absence of inclination to error), and *physical equilibrium* (exemption from suffering and death). Yet man remained free, and consequently, like the angels, capable of sinning if he so wished.

As with the angels, man's sin was essentially the sin of pride, the guilty desire to make himself equal to God.

When we survey as a whole the lessons embodied in these opening chapters of Genesis, we surely cannot withhold our admiration and respect for the magnificent visions and, above all, for the profound teachings which they convey to us.

It may truly be said that the illumination they provide permeates all the rest of the Bible, and that the whole of Christian dogma is implicit in these divine pages. The rapid comparison which we shall make between Genesis and the ancient mythologies will bring into even greater relief the superiority of the Scriptures over all other products of the human mind.

OTHER BIBLICAL TEXTS ON THE CREATION

Genesis is far from being the only book in the Bible to mention the creation. Indeed we shall find it most interesting to examine the other texts in which the creation is described, precisely in order to discover what is essential and what is accessory in the narrative, or rather the narratives according to our view, of Genesis. For example, nowhere else is the creation described as occupying "six days". The only object of this feature was, in the opinion of modern commentators, to enforce the "sacred rest of the Sabbath". Never more shall we be told that God needed six days for the task of creation, nor that he felt the need to "rest" after the six days, as if he were tired out by his labours! All this is a feature of the popular way of telling a story. On the contrary, the later texts will be at pains to emphasize the divine omnipotence exercising itself in the creation, the supreme wisdom presiding over all things, and the dignity of man as the corner stone of the whole creation.

Let us now quote the most exciting of these biblical revelations.

We can begin with the Book of Job; we need concern ourselves only with Chapters 38 to 41, which are a blaze of poetry. Job and his friends have ended their discussion.

"Then, from the midst of a whirlwind, the Lord gave Job his answer. Here is one that must ever be clouding the truth of things with words ill considered! Strip, then, and enter the lists; it is my turn to ask questions now, thine to answer them. From what vantage-point wast thou watching, when I laid the foundations of the earth? Tell me, whence comes this sure knowledge of thine? Tell me, since thou art so wise, was it thou or I designed earth's plan, measuring it out with the line? How came its base to stand so firm; who laid its corner stone?"

After this glowing apostrophe, God describes his work. It was he who hollowed out the sea, and set his bounds around it. It was he who created light, who sowed the firmament with stars, who covered the earth with all kinds of animals, who made the lion, the raven, the wild ass, the ostrich, the horse, the eagle and all the monsters of the deep. A flood of imagery bathes this seemingly random recital. Never has there been so splendid a description of the work of the Creator. And when God has finished speaking, Job in his prostration adores the Almighty in these words: "I acknowledge it, thou canst do all thou wilt, and no thought is too difficult for thee. . . . Now I am all remorse, I do penance in dust and ashes" (Job 42. 2, 6).

The same note is sounded in the Psalms.

Take first Psalm 8, attributed to David:

O Lord, our Master, how the majesty of thy name fills the earth! Thy greatness is high above heaven itself. Thou hast made the lips of children, of infants at the breast, vocal with praise, to confound thy enemies; to silence malicious and revengeful tongues. I look up at those heavens of thine, the work of thy hands, at the moon and the stars, which thou hast set in their places; what is man that thou shouldst remember him? What is Adam's breed, that it should claim thy care? Thou hast placed him only a little below the angels, crowning him with glory and honour, and bidding him rule over the works of thy hands. Thou hast put them all under his dominion, the sheep and the cattle, and the wild beasts besides; the birds in the sky, and the fish in the sea, that travel by the sea's paths.

The whole of Psalm 103 is a hymn to the Creator couched in the same terms. It opens with almost the same words: "O Lord my God, what magnificence is thine! Glory and beauty are thy clothing!" But it deals with creation in much greater detail than Psalm 8. This sacred song follows closely the priestly narrative in Genesis, but, as we have remarked, abstains from mentioning the "six days". It describes the creation of light, which is compared to God's "garment", and of the heavens which is like a "curtain thy hand unfolds". The clouds are his "chariot". The winds are his "angels", fire and flame his "servants". At his rebuking word the waters "cowered" and "fled away" at the voice of his thunder "leaving the mountain heights to rise, the valleys to sink into their appointed place". He causes there to be "torrents flooding to the glens, watercourses among the hills that give drink to every wild beast". The birds will "roost beside them". It is God who makes grass to grow for the cattle, and for man, too, the earth "must put forth her shoots, if he is to bring corn out from her bosom; if there is to be wine that will rejoice man's heart...." And at the end the psalmist echoes the opening words of his song: "What diversity, Lord, in thy creatures! What wisdom has designed them all! There is nothing on earth but gives proof of thy creative power! ... Glory be to the Lord for ever.... While life lasts, I will sing in the Lord's

honour; my praise shall be his while I have breath to praise
him!"

The same sentiments are expressed in Psalms 135, 137 and
138. In this last the inspired poet praises God alone for all
that man is and all that man is able to do.

> Author, thou, of my inmost being, didst thou not form me in
> my mother's womb? I praise thee for thy wondrous fashioning,
> for all the wonders of thy creation. Of my soul thou hast full
> knowledge, and this mortal frame had no mysteries for thee,
> who didst contrive it in secret, devise its pattern, there in the
> dark recesses of the earth. All my acts thy eyes have seen, all
> are set down already in thy record; my days were numbered
> before ever they came to be.

The recurrent theme of the Psalms is that God made all
things by his word alone. "Let all these praise the Lord; it was
his command that created them" (Ps. 148. 5).

The Book of Proverbs attributes the works of God to
Wisdom, whom he had begotten before the beginning of time.
The following passage, readily applied by the liturgy to the
Blessed Virgin, has a close affinity with the eternal generation
of the Word spoken of by St John:

> The Lord made me his when first he went about his work,
> at the birth of time, before his creation began. Long, long ago,
> before earth was fashioned, I held my course. Already I lay
> in the womb, when the depths were not yet in being, when no
> springs of water had yet broken; when I was born, the moun-
> tains had not yet sunk on their firm foundations, and there
> were no hills; nor yet had he made the earth, or the rivers, or
> the solid framework of the world. I was there when he built the
> heavens, when he fenced in the waters with a vault inviolable,
> when he fixed the sky overhead, and levelled the fountain-
> springs of the deep. I was there when he enclosed the sea within
> its confines, forbidding the waters to transgress their assigned
> limits, when he poised the foundations of the world. I was at
> his side, a master-workman, my delight increasing with each
> day, as I made play before him all the while; made play in this
> world of dust, with the sons of Adam for my play-fellows.
> (Proverbs 8. 23–31.)

No words could better express the sovereign ease with which God made all things: for him it was "wisdom at play". To him it is no effort, no fatigue. There is no longer any question of his "resting" the seventh day. In this sense we may conclude that the inspired authors who wrote after Moses were not afraid of altering their presentation of the details, while at the same time giving utterance to the same fundamental truths.

Nowhere do we find any trace of pantheism or polytheism. Everywhere we find the same conception of God, expressed in a pure and majestic doctrine.

Precisely the same ideas, and often the same imagery, are found in the magnificent description of creation contained in Chapters 42 and 43 of Ecclesiasticus. The latter chapter contains this moving conclusion:

"Say we much as we will, of what needs to be said our words come short; be this the sum of all our saying, He is in all things. To what end is all our boasting? He, the Almighty, is high above all that he has made." (Ecclus. 43. 29–30.)

Such is the Old Testament doctrine of the creation. However magnificent, it was to be further enriched by St John by the addition of two important elements.

In the first place, in the first words of his Gospel he gives a personal name to that mysterious and sublime Wisdom whom we have seen "playing" before the Creator as he performed his work of creation.

This Wisdom is indeed none other than the Word, the very Son of God in the bosom of the eternal Trinity.

St John, obviously not unintentionally, employs a formula reminiscent of the story of the creation. Genesis says: "At the beginning of time", and St John says: "At the beginning of time" (that is, before all things, when there was as yet nothing) "the Word already was, and God had the Word abiding with him" (as was said of Wisdom), "and the Word was God. He abode at the beginning of time with God. It was through him that all things came into being, and without him came nothing that has come to be. In him there was life, and that life was the light of men."

These sublime words are repeated daily by all priests of the Roman rite at the conclusion of the sacrifice of the Mass. They surpass in grandeur, and above all in precision, the opening words of Genesis. But it was the same St John who, in his first Epistle, made an even more illuminating addition, when he said, "God is love; and he who dwells in love dwells in God, and God in him" (1 John 4. 16).

This time the last reference is to God, and to the reasons for which he not only created the world and man, but redeemed it by his Son, and showed the way to bliss, which consists in being "like him", in contemplating and possessing him to all eternity, provided one has lived and died in his love. Of this truth all the Christian saints have possessed a marvellous knowledge. This is the meaning of the dying words of Teresa of Lisieux: "It is love alone that matters."

THE CREATION IN CHRISTIAN TRADITION

By this means, not only is creation *ex nihilo* asserted, together with the incomprehensible omnipotence of God, but an insight is afforded not only into the inmost nature of God but into the motives, or rather the sole motive, which led him to the act of creation: *God is love*.

We have now quoted the chief passages from the Bible relating to the creation of the world and of man. It remains to assemble the entire series of pronouncements by the Fathers and the Councils of the Church which make up what theologians call *tradition*. As is explained in the volume of this series devoted to the subject, by tradition we mean not the anonymous chain along which dogmas are transmitted, but on the contrary the collective testimony of the Fathers and writers of the Church which is crowned by the decisions of councils and popes. Tradition closely adheres to Holy Writ, and is based upon it. It provides an authoritative commentary and an interpretation of the biblical texts.

Since the Fathers wrote at great length on the subject we are discussing, we need quote only a few important passages, leaving the rest to be taken for granted. We shall then adduce the henceforth irrevocable decisions of the councils, in which the Church's doctrine is presented to the faithful.

The principal patristic views concerning the creation of the world and of man are the following.

God is the creator of all things. Creation took place *ex nihilo*, that is to say in the absence of any pre-existing matter. God alone is able to create. The act of creation is beyond the power of any creature whatsoever. In the act of creating, God remains entirely free. He creates in accordance with his own innate "ideas". He creates out of pure benevolence, that is, out of love, in order to show forth his perfection. The world is not eternal. It had a beginning. God is not the author of evil. In the beginning creation included immaterial spirits called angels, who are superior to man, but of their own free will have divided themselves into good angels and evil angels or devils.

Man is the highest created being in the visible world. He consists of a body and of an immaterial and immortal soul. He was created immediately by God, acting without any agent. All mankind is descended from one original pair. Our first parents were created in a supernatural state. They were endowed with original justice, exempt from the lusts of the flesh, not subject to the necessity of dying. It is through their disobedience that they find themselves in their present fallen state, from which only the grace of Christ can rescue them.

THE TEACHING OF ST AUGUSTINE

The summary given above contains the essentials of the patristic tradition; but more must be said of one of the Fathers, St Augustine.

In his commentary on the sixth verse of Psalm 134, this great Doctor of the Church says: "We are bound steadfastly (*inconcusse*) to believe and profess that every created thing in the heavens or on earth, in the sea or in the deeps, was made by God, for as the Psalm says: 'Whatsoever the Lord pleased he hath done, in heaven, in earth, in the sea, and in all the deeps.' And if he did all things he did them not perforce, since it is written that whatsoever the Lord pleases, he does. The cause of all that he does is in his own will. You build a house because, if you were unwilling to build it, you would have nowhere to live. It is therefore need, and not your own free will, that makes you build it."[1]

The same explanation is constantly employed throughout St Augustine's writings. In one of his earliest works, an unfinished commentary on Genesis written in 393–4, he says:

"Catholic teaching bids us profess that the Holy Trinity is one only God, and that he made and created all that is, in so far as it is, in such a manner that every spiritual or bodily creature, or in the words of Scripture visible or invisible creature, is born not of God, but made by God out of nothing. It follows that nothing in the creature appertains to the Trinity, but everything was made by the Trinity. Whence it is forbidden to say or to believe of any creature whatsoever that it is consubstantial or co-eternal with God" (*P.L.* 34, 221).

It will be remembered that in his *Confessions* St Augustine, after recalling the graces that brought him to the Christian faith and to baptism, devotes several chapters to a series of meditations on the mysteries of faith. Here is what he says on the subject of the creation:

> Such then are the heaven and the earth. They cry out that they were made, because they are subject to change. Everything that was not made, and yet is, exhibits nothing that has not been, which is the same as to be subject to change. Therefore they cry out that they did not make themselves. "We are, only because we were made. For previously we were not, and consequently were not in a position to make ourselves." And these same words of theirs are the very proof of what they say. Therefore thou, O Lord, because thou art beautiful, madest them, for they are beautiful; because thou art good, for they are good because thou hadst being, for they also have being.

[1] Migne, *Patrologia Latina*, 37, 1745 (hereinafter quoted as *P.L.*).

But they are neither beautiful nor good, nor do they exist, after thy manner who createdst them, and in comparison with thee they are neither beautiful nor good nor endowed with being (*P.L.* 32, 811).

All the teachings of the Fathers are summed up in statements such as these. But St Augustine carried his examination of the biblical texts further than any other of the Fathers, as can be demonstrated from the following very important quotations from his Commentary on Genesis, written between 401 and 415.

In what we have called the "priestly" creation narrative we have seen that God's work of creation was spread over six days; but we suggested that this span of time had a merely ritual significance, and was intended to inculcate the desirability of "resting on the seventh day". It is therefore interesting to observe what St Augustine thought of this passage from Genesis.

"When the Scriptures say of God that he accomplished his task in six days, this in no way contradicts what is said elsewhere (Ecclus. 18. 1), that he created all things together.[1] It is therefore still the same creation that is indicated by these six or seven days, for God made all things at the same time" (*P.L.* 34, 318).

But the most suggestive passage we shall quote from St Augustine is the following, which confers its higher authority on the whole theory of evolution as interpreted in the Christian sense:

Just as in a seed there is to be found at the same time, albeit invisible, all that is to appear later in the tree, so should we imagine the world, after God had created all things together, as carrying within itself all that came to light when day was created: not only the heaven and the earth, with the sun, the moon and the stars which revolve in a circle after their several kinds, but also the earth and the deeps which are subject to

[1] Nowadays we should prefer to say: "He who is to all eternity created all things complete", not "at the same time". Here, however, we are concerned with what St Augustine thought.

irregular movements and form the lower portion of the world. But equally all that the water and the earth have since produced, they already possessed in a potential and causal manner (*potentialiter et causaliter*), before the appearance in the course of time of all that we recognize in these works of God, in whose midst he continues to act without ceasing (*P.L.* 34, 338).

This idea seems to have had a great attraction for St Augustine, who frequently returns to it. It is known as the theory of *seminal* causes, and bears a striking resemblance to Teilhard de Chardin's theory of "guided evolution". Between 388 and 390, and therefore shortly after his conversion, St Augustine had already put forward this theory in his controversy with the Manichaeans.

Ten years later we again encounter it in his Commentary on Genesis. One of the most explicit passages in all his works is to be found in the "Questions on the Heptateuch", which were written in 419, ten years later still; and with this quotation we shall end our examination of St Augustine's views.

In all corporeal things, through all the elements which compose the world, there are to be found certain seminal causes (*seminariae rationes*), thanks to which, at the right time and in the appropriate circumstance, they burst forth (*prorumpunt*) in their foreseen kinds according to their modes and ends. And it is for this reason that the angels who bring this about cannot be called the creators of the animals, any more than a farmer can be called the creator of the harvest or of the trees which rise from the earth, although he knows how to produce those opportunities and causes which bring them to birth. Now what the farmer does visibly, the angels do invisibly. But God is the one and only creator, who created the causes themselves and inserted the seminal causes into things (*P.L.* 34, 602).

DECISIONS OF THE CHURCH

Before proceeding to the comparison between Christian and pagan theories of origin which will occupy us in our next chapter, we shall first set out the invariable and irrevocable teachings of the Church regarding the creation of all things by God. These decisions were reaffirmed by the Vatican Council in 1870. As is customary they assume two forms, one positive and the other negative, consisting in the condemnation of errors rejected by Christian doctrine.

In its positive form the doctrine of creation is set out in the first chapter of the "Constitution of the Catholic Faith".

> The Holy Catholic Apostolic and Roman Church believes and confesses that there is but one true and living God.... This one true God, by his omnipotent goodness and virtue, not in order to enhance his beatitude, nor to increase his perfection, but to manifest it by the blessings which he dispenses to all creatures, with a completely free intention, created at one and the same time, at the beginning of time, the two creatures, namely the angelic world and our world, and lastly the human creature in so far as he is made all of one soul and body.

In its negative form, erroneous doctrines are condemned in the four following canons:

> (1) If anyone denies that the only true God is the creator and the lord of all things visible and invisible, let him be anathema.
>
> (2) If anyone is so bold as to affirm that nothing exists beyond matter, let him be anathema.
>
> (3) If anyone says that God and created things have only one and the same substance or essence, or that the divine essence becomes all things by its manifestation and evolution, or lastly that God is the universal or indeterminate being which, by determining itself, constitutes the totality of things arranged in their genera, species and individuals, let him be anathema.
>
> (4) If anyone refuses to profess that the world and all the things which it contains, both spiritual and material, were according to the totality of their substance created out of nothing by God; or if he says that God created, not by an act of will freed from all necessity, but from the same necessity as that whereby he loves himself; or if he denies that the world

was created to the glory of God, let him be anathema."
(Denzinger-U, 1801–5.)

We have nothing to add to documents such as these. It only
remains for us to compare, in a final chapter, the facts of the
Christian faith with the facts of mythology, philosophy and
modern science.

CHAPTER V

COMPARISONS, AGREE-MENTS AND DISAGREEMENTS

CREATION IN CHRISTIANITY AND MYTHOLOGY

We have admitted that the Bible contains some mythical elements. This fact need cause no surprise. Myth was man's first answer to the absorbing problem of the origins of things. Myth is an attempt at explanation: it therefore assumes that there is an explanation, which it is man's duty to pursue. Myth would have been a bad thing only if it had succeeded in halting man's search. But though for centuries it satisfied the desire for knowledge, it neither stifled nor extinguished it. Myth was a forerunner of philosophy and science, to the extent to which it attempted to provide an objective and intelligible explanation of things.

Nothing more natural than that the word of God should have adapted itself to this primitive form of human philosophy and science. God does not take the place of man. As St Augustine would have said, God leaves the "seminal causes" to develop and produce their effects, according as the passage of time provides the opportunity.

But beneath the archaic, familiar and popular forms of the myths, revelation was already at work conveying "the fundamental truths necessary to the economy of salvation".

It is for the exegetes and the theologians and, in the last resort, for the teaching authority of the Church, to discriminate between what is mythical in the biblical texts and what in the myth deserves to be retained as true. That a serpent spoke is the myth; that the temptation took place, that its author was the devil, and that first the woman and then the man yielded to it is the teaching of revelation which will stand for ever.

In the apt words of a contemporary exegete: "God chose as his interpreter the ancients and the peoples of the east: all the scandals of the west today derive from that fact. . . . For the full acceptance of his Word, what is required is a change of heart."[1]

BABYLONIAN MYTHOLOGY AND THE BOOK OF GENESIS

We will now return to the Babylonian myth of the creation of the world. The poem containing this myth is known as *Enuma elis*. As we pointed out, its obvious intention was to exalt Marduk, the god of Babylon, above all the other gods, with the object of securing for Babylon the mastery of the whole world.

In this mythical poem we find features directly opposed to the Bible narrative. One is polytheism, another is the origin of the gods. They are the offspring of Chaos, that is to say of Apsu and Tiamat. When their life is threatened for disturbing Apsu's repose, the gods declare war. Anu, the first to advance, takes fright and beats a cowardly retreat. The god Marduk advances in his turn, armed from top to toe. He pierces his adversary Tiamat with an arrow, and out of the corpse makes the firmament above and mankind below. To make man he uses clay and the blood of a god.

Contrasted with this involved and childish story, from which all that can be gathered is the general idea of order triumphing over disorder, the biblical account of the creation stands out

[1] Here and subsequently in this chapter we follow the closely reasoned article by A. Gelin in *L'Ami du clergé*, September 6th, 1956. The above quotation is from P. Benoît's commentary on the Encyclical *Divino afflante Spiritu* in *Initiation biblique* (Paris, 1954), p. 42–43.

in incomparable beauty. Polytheism is replaced by the purest monotheism. God the creator has no need to wage war. He speaks, and all things obey him. With a single word he creates and orders everything. The spirituality of the ideas, the dignity of the style and the splendour of the imagery raise this first page of Genesis immeasurably above the Babylonian and all the other myths we have recorded.

Stress has sometimes been laid on the fact that the Babylonians allowed man a share in the divine nature, in that the blood of a god was mixed with the clay of which his body was composed.

But here there are two things to be considered: (1) the mention of clay, and (2) the presence of a divine element in man.

THE CREATION OF MAN

In the older of the two biblical narratives God uses earthen clay (*ha'-adama*) to form the first man (*ha'-adam*) whose very name is derived from the substance employed. And God breathes in man's nostrils a breath of life which makes him a *nefesh*, or living creature.

For a long time man had known how to work in clay. Pottery was one of the first arts practised by the human race, next to that of stone-cutting. In the palaeolithic caves there were skilful sculptors of living forms, particularly of steatopygous female statuettes which may have been fertility emblems. Consequently it was easy to imagine a potter-god. The figure occurs in many mythologies, and is found not only in Babylonia but among the Maoris and others.

In the Bible, this theme of the potter-God is partly intended to express man's dependence on God. St Paul so interprets it when he speaks of predestination as of God's absolute freedom of action with respect to the "vessels of clay" which his hands have formed: "Is the pot to ask the potter, Why hast thou fashioned me thus?" (Romans 9. 20).

On the other hand, clay is an admirable symbol of man's frailty. But what concerns us principally in man is his higher life, by virtue of which he is truly man. It is this life which, according to Genesis, God communicates by the "breath of life" (*ruach*), which was later to be translated as "soul".

A comparison between the Biblical and the Babylonian narratives reveals a total divergence in aim.

In the Bible, the "divine breath" is a kindly gift and a mark of honour. God makes man in his image and likeness because he intends man to be the corner-stone of the visible creation and the king of all creatures on earth. It is God's goodness that is at work, and it is that goodness which St John calls Love.

We saw in the Babylonian story that there was war between the gods. During the battle certain gods had been slain. Thenceforth the survivors are oppressed with a sense of guilt: they had brought death into the world. How then can they rid themselves of this guilt, except by a rite of transference? It was in order to transfer their guilt that the gods created the four original human pairs. The blood of the defeated god Kingu will transmit the guilt to mankind; by this means mankind will become subject to death, and will at the same time deliver the gods from death. Thus the creation of man, far from being an act of love, is an act of the most commonplace selfishness. We are in the world of phantasmagoria.

What a noble conception of God and man is revealed by the Bible narrative, compared with the degraded idea of both which emerges from the Babylonian myth!

We need not pursue the parallel. The biblical story of creation, even in its most primitive features, is infinitely superior to all the mythologies.

We shall now see how it stands comparison with the highest achievements of human philosophy.

THE BIBLE COSMOGONY AND PHILOSOPHY

In the chapter devoted to expounding the philosophical theories of the origins of the world and of man, we confined ourselves to the ancient philosophies. Among these some attained to magnificent heights. Plato and Aristotle are still, and always will be, regarded as supremely great thinkers.

The attitude of Christian theology towards the great philosophies of the past was at the same time extremely intelligent and very human. The Fathers of the Church drew largely on the teaching of the schools: but in so doing they preserved their own freedom. Thanks to the revelation contained in the Bible, they felt themselves to be in possession of irrefutable truths: we remember St Augustine's term, *inconcusse*.

Christian scholars thus remained "steadfastly" attached to the teachings of the Bible. They can never be otherwise when they enter the fields of philosophy or science. But in future, though this has not always been the case in the past, they will do well to avoid a confusion of spheres and a mixture of disciplines. There can be such a thing as a "Christian philosophy", and in another volume of this series it is explained how and in what sense such an expression can rightly be used. On the contrary there has never been, and never will be, a "Christian science", but only plain science.

The truth is that philosophy, science and theology operate on different planes. What our faith teaches us is that there can be no real opposition between these different planes or between the branches of study which each pursues.

Our purpose in contrasting the facts of science with the facts of faith was not at all to show that there is any agreement between them. This, as we pointed out, was the error of "concordism", and great care must be taken in future not to fall into it again. But it remains our duty to withstand any attack by science on faith, and to assert the principle of non-opposition between the two.

This we shall now attempt to do, following the same order observed in dealing with the latest scientific discoveries.

THEOLOGY AND ASTRONOMY

Our first encounter was with astronomy and the enormous changes brought about by it in our conception of man's place in time and space.

Quite recently a number of the most eminent astronomers

have published their conclusions in the September 1956 issue of *The Scientific American*. The purely scientific facts brought forward in their statements need not detain us, though they are of absorbing interest. But among the articles there is one that deals with cosmogony, which almost of necessity impinges on the teachings of the faith. Two main theories are submitted for consideration. One is propounded by Fred Hoyle of Cambridge University, and is known as the theory of the "steady-state universe". It leads to the following conclusions, described by the author himself as "startling", namely that the universe had no beginning and will have no end, that space and time are infinite, and that matter is constantly being created in space.

It must be admitted that it would be difficult to reconcile this theory with the Christian faith. Nevertheless it is far from being atheistic, since it postulates a process of eternal and ceaseless creation.

This theory, however, does not seem to meet with favour from the astronomers. The second theory is propounded by Allan A. Sandage, and postulates an "expanding-contracting universe". It agrees that five and a half thousand million years ago all known matter was condensed into a single primal atom, a superdense state, which exploded, its constituent elements being catapulted into space so as to give birth to the at least two thousand million galaxies of which our universe is composed. But according to Sandage all the evidence goes to show that the initial explosion must have been counterbalanced by a braking action operated on the recession of the galaxies by the force of gravity exerted by the remaining unexploded matter. It is as if a ball were thrown into the air attached to a piece of elastic. The elastic would retard the ball in its flight, and finally bring it back to its starting point. Thus we should have a process of expansion-contraction.

Sandage himself concludes his exposition of the expanding-contracting theory of the universe with these words, which recall the old Stoic idea of "eternal recurrence": "If the expansion of the universe is decelerating at the rate our present data suggest, the expansion will eventually stop and contraction will begin."

This first conclusion would not matter very much, and would not deserve mention here, since we are concerned solely with the origins of man. But the author goes on: "If it returns to a superdense state and explodes again, then in the next cycle of oscillation, some fifteen billion years hence, we may all find ourselves again pursuing our present tasks."

This can only mean that man is merely a constantly recurring incident within a closed cycle lasting about fifteen thousand million years.

However, the author himself adopts a conjectural tone, and it would obviously be futile, from the point of view of the Christian religion, to discuss so uncertain and improbable a hypothesis.

It has not yet been proved that the universe is "contracting."[1] But even if the fact were established, there is nothing to prove that the universe would purely and simply return to its starting point from a primal atom in a state of superdensity. Finally, if such a thing were to occur, the further assumption would have to be made that this atom would again burst in exactly the same way, and that in the course of an immensely long period of evolution man would appear at exactly the same moment and in the same manner, without any variation whatsoever.

A universe of this kind might be justly described as no more than "everlasting nonsense".

Passing now from astronomical time to astronomical space, we encounter the objection raised by an astronomer and already quoted in Chapter III.

"One must be the victim of incurable anthropocentrism to believe that the slightest importance attaches to the race of thinking microbes inhabiting an imperceptible globe revolving round this sun."

----

[1] At the time of writing, October 1956, Sandage's conclusions have been rejected, following observations carried out by William A. Baum at the Mount Palomar Observatory.

What can theology reply to this? Must she abandon her "unshakeable" certainties, that is to say the dogmas of the Trinity, the Incarnation and the Redemption, on the grounds that man is merely a "thinking microbe"?

Theology in her turn will reply: One must be the victim of an excessive concern for *quantity* to disregard so completely the supreme importance of *quality*. Granted that man is no more than a microbe. Pascal called him "a reed". But he is a "thinking microbe", a circumstance which confers upon him not equality to, but superiority over, the entire material universe, whatever size it may be. In fact, a false problem is created by the attempt to discredit thought on account of the small space occupied in the universe by the material organism which is its vehicle.

Pascal has answered this argument in the famous passage in the *Pensées* describing the "three orders", from which we quote the following extract:

> But there are some who can only admire worldly greatness, as though there were no intellectual greatness; and others who only admire intellectual greatness, as though there were not infinitely higher things in wisdom.
>
> All bodies, the firmament, the stars, the earth and its kingdoms, are not equal to the lowest mind; for mind knows all these and itself; and these bodies are nothing.
>
> All bodies together, and all minds together, and all their products, are not equal to the least feeling of charity. This is of an order infinitely more exalted.
>
> From all bodies together, we cannot obtain one little thought; this is impossible, and of another order. From all bodies and minds, we cannot produce a feeling of true charity; this is impossible, and of another and supernatural order.[1]

We could quote Péguy to the same effect. Indeed, if we imagine an astronomer at the eye-piece of the giant Mount Palomar telescope which has provided the latest discoveries in astronomy, it might well be asked whether the greater marvel

---

[1] *Pascal's Pensées*, Everyman edition, p. 235.

is to be found at the eye-piece or the aperture end of the telescope.

Our contention is that it will be found at the eye-piece end. The "thinking microbe" who stands at an instrument which is the product of a wealth of scientific research and technique and of a vast expenditure of capital and human labour, the astronomer whose enormously extended range of vision plumbs the furthest recesses of space, is to our eyes a more astonishing spectacle than the huge agglomerations of atoms making up the nebulae, each one of which is but a replica of the others. We know but little about these nebulae. In particular, we do not know whether each galaxy trails, like our own sun, at least one planet inhabited by beings akin to ourselves. In this field any supposition is permissible, and none is contradicted by theology. But the enormous extent of the space occupied by the stars, and the terrifying distances at which they are situated, are powerless to induce us to abandon our conviction that divine grace is superior to human nature, and that human nature with its endowment of intelligence and freedom is superior to mere matter.

In short, none of all this presents any problem. We are impressed neither by "astronomical" figures nor by the thousands of millions of years of the life of the universe compared with the few hundreds of thousands of the life of mankind. The appearance of man was a greater event than anything that has since happened on this earth; and in the vast setting of the universe, the appearance of a man on the earth was a novelty surpassing all the aggregations of atoms whirling in the midst of the distant galaxies.

So much for our first branch of science, absorbing though it be. Astronomy in no wise contradicts our faith. On the contrary, it strengthens it. Anything that provides a loftier idea of God and of man is favourable to that faith. And this is precisely the function of astronomy: to enlarge and enrich our conception of God and of man.

THE PROBLEM OF EVOLUTION AND TRANSFORMISM

Can we say as much of the modern scientific theories of evolution and transformism?

Here we encounter one of the most delicate problems that we shall have to examine.

There is no doubt that the question of evolution has for too long been bedevilled by philosophical and religious prejudices. The time has come when these matters should be discussed with the full intellectual freedom which theology always accords to science. We maintain that the Catholic faith is so all-embracing, so regardful of facts and of science which records and classifies them, that it can easily adapt and absorb any established fact in the field of science.

When the evolutionary hypothesis was first propounded (and we must not forget that it is not and cannot be anything more than a hypothesis), it was unfortunately used exclusively to attack religion. When in 1865 Clémence Royer published a French translation of Darwin's famous *Origin of Species*, she did not conceal her intention of putting an end to religious belief in the name of the discoveries of science.

"I certainly believe", she wrote, "in revelation, but in a permanent revelation of man, to man, by man; a rational revelation which is no more than the resultant of the advances in contemporary scientific thought; a revelation always incomplete and relative, which is brought about by the acquisition of new truths, and even more by the elimination of ancient errors."

So far, so good. But Clémence Royer did not confine herself to generalities. Among the "ancient errors", and at their head, she included "mysticism", the fruit of the teachings of Jesus.

"The teaching of Jesus", she writes, "was a sign of the times. It was a portent of death for the people who listened to it, and whose downfall it hastened. In general, mysticism is a kind of disease which afflicts the human race, a kind of exhaustion and decline. Wherever it breaks out it leads to nervous prostration and moral apathy, combined with mental excitability. Finally it is a morbid passion of the old age of a people, and an invariable symptom of social decay."

We can afford to smile at an outburst like this, which is flatly contradicted by the facts of history. It is inspired by an anti-religious fanaticism which is open to precisely the same charges which it brings against mysticism. In any case, nothing could be more unscientific than the language employed by Clémence Royer. Science holds no brief either for or against mysticism. Its function is to observe the facts, classify them, and reduce them to their natural laws.

Whether or not evolution has taken place is to be decided from a study of the facts. As to whether such evolution, assuming it to have taken place, leads to the denial or the assertion of the existence of God, that is a question for philosophy and for metaphysics, which will have to reckon with revealed religion.

Now a distinguished contemporary palaeontologist, Teilhard de Chardin, has ventured on the bold assertion that there has been an evolution of species, but that this evolution did not come about by chance but was obviously "guided", that it was directed towards an end, and mounted step by step towards what he calls the "Omega point". This point he identifies with the idea of God, with Jesus Christ.

Without committing ourselves to such a decided opinion, we may be allowed to suggest that the theory of evolution is not only not opposed to the idea of God, but necessitates it even more than the theory of the fixity of species. Indeed the believer in the fixity of species may be brought to admit that the world is eternal, that it has been "fixed" once and for all without the possibility of change, and that any movements that may be observed in it are mere appearance, repetition, "tautology" so to speak. But the believer in evolution is bound to postulate a beginning. Evolution without a beginning is as self-contradictory as a square circle. If it actually had no beginning, it must, from all eternity, have had an eternity behind it; in other words it must have exhausted all its possibilities of development.

Furthermore, if evolution, inasmuch as it is not yet finished, must have had a beginning, it requires, in order that it may begin, the intervention of a creator.

But if in addition we agree with Teilhard de Chardin that evolution is "guided", then we must postulate a "guide". Without this no "guidance" is conceivable. And there can be no other possible guide than the omnipotent Mind of a God. At this point we must examine the problem more closely.

A BRIEF EXAMINATION OF TRANSFORMISM

The sciences of palaeontology and prehistory are necessarily concerned only with man's body, to the neglect of his soul. If we arrange a set of human fossils in a single ascending order, it is easy to see that, following the chronology of the geological strata, they are becoming progressively more "human". What undoubtedly emerges from a comparison of fossils is the uninterrupted development of a larger brain. No science, however, can explain how the specific human intelligence made its first appearance, any more than it can explain how a human soul comes into existence today. When therefore science speaks of man's appearing, it is simply noting the juxtaposition alongside this or that fossil of artefacts assumed to be the products of human intelligence. Nevertheless it remains beyond the scope of science as such to explain how such an intelligence came to be substantially united with a particular body.

Here we reach the most difficult part of our argument.

Radical transformism asserts that the whole man—body and soul—is the product of evolution. But in making this assertion it clearly oversteps the bounds of pure science. Side by side with radical transformism there is room for a spiritual transformism which provides for the intervention of God in the creation of the soul.

CREATIONISM

This theory calls for as precise an explanation as is possible. When we speak of an intervention on the part of God, we do not of course for one moment entertain the childish notion of a God who acts spasmodically, by fits and starts as it were; who relies on the laws of nature for the ordinary routine of the universe, but is galvanized into activity when he finds an obstacle in the path. We need not insult the theologians by supposing them capable of such a ridiculous idea. Throughout this book we have fought against the Aristotelian theory that action is unworthy of the Prime Mover, with the result that he can act on things only in so far as he is their final cause.

We have already quoted the profound saying of Christ with reference to the Sabbath rest: "My Father has never ceased working, and I too must be at work" (John 5. 17). When we speak of God's *intervening* to create the soul, we mean that in the course of his continuous activity without which the laws of nature would cease to operate, we pass from one degree to another. We are faced with what Teilhard de Chardin calls the passage from the simple "biosphere" to the "noosphere", from the biological to the mental plane. The human soul is something totally different from what we call, by analogy and without understanding what we mean by it, the *animal soul*, or Claude Bernard's *guiding idea*.

The "animal soul" is handed on by the simple act of propagation. This doctrine is known as *traducianism*. A few of the early Fathers believed in the applicability of traducianism to the human soul, but this opinion was rejected by the common teaching of the Church, which professes *creationism*, that is, the directly divine origin by creation of every human soul.

According to this doctrine the soul cannot derive from the body, nor from any physical seed. It comes directly from God, who is the fulfilment of all the laws of nature. By this we mean that the *noosphere* represents a new stage in the created universe, a new "kingdom", the "human kingdom" as distinct from the "animal kingdom".

In the context of creationism there is no reason why the human body should not have sprung from the "clay of the earth", as the Bible says, by a process of lengthy and slow evolution. We must not forget that a million years are as nothing in the sight of an eternal God. Indeed we have seen that St Augustine, one of the profoundest and most famous of Christian thinkers, while acknowledging that all things were created at the same time, believed that by the will of God they contained "seminal causes" destined to produce their effects at the appropriate time.

Without lapsing into concordism, it may be granted that such a conception leaves a clear field for any evolutionary theory of the emergence of man.

Moreover, the Church has recently issued a clear statement on this matter in the Encyclical *Humani generis* of Pius XII, dated August 12th, 1950:

"The teaching of the Church leaves the doctrine of evolution an open question, as long as it confines its speculations to the development, from other living matter already in existence, of the human body. (That souls are immediately created by God is a view which the Catholic faith imposes on us.)"

The road is therefore clear. Science is completely free to carry on within her own field. All that is required is that she should not encroach beyond that field. Thus it is perfectly permissible to call oneself a "spiritual and Catholic transformist." But one is a transformist only for scientific reasons, and by no means for reasons of a religious or even philosophic order.

There remains, however, one outstanding problem, that of monogenism versus polygenism.

MONOGENISM OR POLYGENISM?

In the preceding chapter we said that almost all scientists are monophyletists, since they believe that man as we know him today derives from a single phylum, or from a single more or less remote animal stock. But we added that the great majority are polygenists, since they believe that from the single stock there issued, either simultaneously or at different times, and in different places, several human pairs from which present-day man originated.

We have already explained their reasons for holding these views.

(1) The general laws of evolution suggest a "fan-wise" process involving the almost simultaneous appearance of new forms.

(2) The appearance of mankind in the form of a single pair would have provided an extremely narrow base-line for the development of the new species.

(3) The Adam of theology would have had to be *Homo sapiens* from the very beginning, whereas prehistory places his appearance after that of other creatures who were certainly human though less perfect than man.

(4) The Adam of theology must have been born fully adult, a proposition which is meaningless to a prehistorian.

Are these arguments conclusive? It would not appear so. And here are some of the replies which a monogenist scientist (for such there are) might well make to them.

COUNTER-ARGUMENTS

In the first place, although the laws of general evolution may *suggest* that a "fan-wise" mutation might account for the appearance of the new species, too little is known of the details of these laws to *oblige* us to believe in this kind of mutation. In point of fact we are completely ignorant of how the "sudden mutations" in the evolution of life are brought about, nor do we know whether they operated in the same way to produce the human species.

It must, however, be admitted that though man, as we know him, is an almost solitary figure from a zoological point of view, yet "he was not unattended in his cradle".

"There can no longer be any doubt", says Teilhard de Chardin, "that among the rocks and forests of a clearly defined but immense area extending from southern Africa to southern

China and the Malay Archipelago, the Anthropoids were, at the close of the Tertiary period, far more numerous than they are today. In addition to the gorilla, the chimpanzee and the orang-utang, who are now driven back, like the Australian aborigine and the negrillo, to their last strongholds, there flourished at that time a great many other large Primates. And among these species the African Australopithecus, for example, seems to have been far closer to man than any living creature now known to us."[1]

Accordingly it may be unequivocally admitted, at least as a hypothesis, that evolution in the direction of man *presents the appearance* of a fan shape.

Yet it remains to be proved that it *was brought about* in precisely this manner. In other words, we have good reason to believe that there were several candidates for the status of "human beings": Sinanthropus, Pithecanthropus, Africanthropus, etc. But we are unable to say whether all of them succeeded in reaching the goal. And even if several did succeed, we cannot be certain that all of them attained to true humanity.

That being so, the remaining arguments for polygeny require no answer. We have provided a sufficiently broad basis for the line of development ending in man. The appearance of *Homo sapiens* may well have been preceded by the appearance of other less perfect human beings whose posterity have failed to survive. Finally, to credit theology with believing in the birth of an adult Adam is an entirely gratuitous charge, once we admit the principle of a line of evolution culminating in a specifically human body.

We may therefore conclude with a quotation from Teilhard de Chardin, who is rightly or wrongly considered one of the most determined champions of polygenism:

"This is why the problem of *monogenism* in the strict sense of the word (but not the problem of *monophyletism*) seems by its very nature to elude science as such. At the distance of time at which man makes his appearance, our intensest scrutiny is

[1] *Le Phénomène humain*, p. 204.

totally unable to discover the presence and activity of one unique pair. So that it might be said that in that gap there is room for anything that may be demanded by a transcendental source of knowledge."[1]

By these last words Teilhard de Chardin clearly intends us to understand that, from the purely scientific point of view, the field lies open to all the findings and doctrines of revealed religion. It is therefore to revelation that we must now turn our attention.

ADAM: INDIVIDUAL OR COLLECTIVE?

Basing ourselves solely on biblical exegesis, Christian tradition and the authority of the Church, can we allow the possibility that the name Adam might designate not an individual but a group? Could it be that Adam and Eve were not one unique pair, but that the two names cover a multiplicity of pairs?

The question would certainly seem to answer itself. Until quite recently, indeed, no one had ever cast the slightest doubt on the uniqueness of the first human pair. One may search the commentators without finding one who held that the names Adam and Eve represented not one pair but a multiplicity of pairs.

This being so, it would be falling back on the most indefensible type of concordism (which is precisely what is to be avoided at all costs) to twist the plain meaning of the Bible texts into agreement with the polygenist hypothesis. Unless one were bent on finding such an agreement, one would have no hesitation in accepting the statements of Genesis, and especially of St Paul, at their face value, and they would mean what the Church has always held them to mean.

In the case of Genesis there is no room for doubt. But St Paul has sometimes been taken to hold that the name Adam is identical with what he calls "the old man". Our own opinion

[1] *Op. cit.*, p. 206, note.

is that this interpretation is as flagrantly false in the case of
St Paul as in the case of Genesis, and we repeat that it is pure
and simple concordism to put forward an interpretation so
foreign to the whole Christian tradition.

On two particular occasions St Paul refers to Adam as the
forefather of mankind. On both occasions he clearly refers to
an *individual*, not a *collective* Adam. Indeed in the Epistle to
the Romans he devotes no fewer than nine verses to working
out a parallel between the work of Adam and the work of
Jesus Christ. Repeatedly he contrasts the two ideas: *through
one man* came sin and death; *through one man* came redemption and life (Romans 5. 12–21). But if in the first case the
words "through one man" can be taken in a collective sense,
the same would have to be true in the second case, which is
absurd. There were not several "wreckers" of the human race,
any more than there were several redeemers.

The oneness of the new Adam is the necessary counterpart
of the oneness of the old Adam. If we adhere strictly to the
natural meaning of the words, eschewing any attempt at concordism, we can only attach to St Paul's words the same meaning they have always borne up to the time when our present
problem obtruded itself.

But St Paul speaks of the first man not only in connection
with original sin. In his speech before the Areopagus it is not
of original sin he is thinking when he mentions, as if it went
without saying, that God made "*of one single stock*, all the
nations that were to dwell over the whole face of the earth"
(Acts 17. 26).

If we turn now to the decrees of the Councils, and particularly of the Council of Trent, we shall see that, when expounding original sin, constant reference is made to *one single man*.

"If anyone says", declares the Council of Trent, "that *the
first man Adam*, after disobeying the commandments of God
in paradise, did not forthwith forfeit that state of holiness and
justice in which he had been established ... let him be
anathema!" (Session V, canon 1).

And again: "If anyone asserts that the prevarication of

Adam harmed *only himself* and not his posterity . . . let him be anathema!" (c. 2).

"If anyone says that this sin of Adam, which was *unique in its origin*, and has become the property of all not by imitation but by transmission, can be removed by natural forces . . . let him be anathema!" (c. 3).

It would clearly be an abuse of language to take these texts as referring to a collective Adam, and not to one single man, Adam the unique forefather of mankind.

THE ENCYCLICAL "HUMANI GENERIS"

It would be easy to provide further evidence of a similar kind, and one might in particular refer to the draft definition prepared for the Vatican Council, but abandoned in the event. But we must add in conclusion that the theory of a collective Adam was formally rejected by Pius XII in his Encyclical *Humani generis* of August 12th, 1950. And since this Encyclical is expressly directed against the theories we have been discussing, we cannot do better than quote the relevant passage in full.

The Pope begins by saying that it is altogether "praise-worthy" that Christian teaching should take into the "fullest consideration" the positive sciences in such matters as are more or less closely related to the truths of the faith. He gives as an example, which we have already quoted, the study of evolution in so far as it deals with the human body and then goes on:

> There are other conjectures about polygenism (as it is called), which leave the faithful no such freedom of choice. Christians cannot lend their support to a theory which involves the exis-tence, after Adam's time, of some earthly race of men, truly so called, who were not descended ultimately from him,[1] or else supposes that Adam was the name given to some group of our

---

[1] This passage must refer to Neanderthal Man, who undoubtedly lived after Adam, and is believed to have been a true man, as explained in a previous chapter.

primordial ancestors. It does not appear how such views can be reconciled with the doctrine of original sin, as this is guaranteed to us by Scripture and tradition, and proposed to us by the Church. Original sin is the result of a a sin committed, in actual historical fact, by an individual man named Adam, and it is a quality native to all of us, only because it has been handed down by descent from him.

The Encyclical then quotes by way of reference the Epistle to the Romans, 5. 12–19, and also canons 1–4 of the fifth Session of the Council of Trent, the first three of which we have mentioned above.

Here it is to be carefully noted that the Pope in the first place is introducing no innovation, but is confining himself to the already established doctrine; nor in the second place is he in any way encroaching on the territory of science, but is content to remain within the Church's own field of teaching authority, which is concerned with the interpretation of the scriptural texts and of Christian tradition. No hindrance is thereby offered to pure scientific investigations. But it is forbidden to distort the biblical or conciliar texts in order to make them square with this or that scientific theory. It is equally forbidden to hold that the Church is in any way incapable of giving a theological decision on her own ground, when such a decision might cause embarrassment to some scientific theory.

It is far from our intention to fall back on the notorious distinction between *law* and *fact*, which for so long exercised the Jansenists. On the contrary, we consider that if the Church, within her own province, propounds a question of law, the facts are thereby involved. And this, in our opinion, is the meaning of the papal Encyclical, with the result that, all things considered, the theory of polygenism cannot be regarded as an accepted fact, even in the scientific field: a conclusion on which both science and theology are agreed.

CONCLUSIONS

To end this discussion, we may be permitted to give a brief summary of our conclusions.

In the first place, throughout this book we have adhered to the view that the problem of man's origins is closely related to the problem of the origin of the world. The principal difficulty we have had to overcome—and we hope to have succeeded in our task—is the separation of anthropogeny from cosmogony. Mythology, philosophy, science and theology itself are at one in viewing the appearance of man as a major incident in the origin of the universe.

In the second place, this incident which mythology and sometimes even philosophy have either treated with contempt or without according it the importance which it now seems to deserve, has continued to loom the larger the more closely it is studied. The myths of Prometheus, of Deucalion and Pyrrha, and others of their kind, bear witness to the scant regard paid to the dignity of man.

As seen from the atomistic materialist standpoint of Democritus, Epicurus and Lucretius, the situation is much the same. Christian theology, on the contrary, has evidently invested the appearance of man with a significance of unparalleled splendour and majesty. With Pascal, philosophy in its turn has assigned to man a station of his own in the universe. As for the scientists, we have, it is true, met with astronomers who refer with disdain to man as a "thinking microbe" confronted with the myriad galaxies, each consisting of millions of stars, extended through space: but we have also been gratified to hear from the lips of a genuine scientist one of the finest imaginable eulogies on man's place in creation.

After discussing the "noosphere", Teilhard de Chardin, in words which we borrow with all the enthusiasm at our command, expressed himself as follows:

"At this point we are confronted with a want of proportion which falsifies any classification of living things (and, indirectly, any attempt to construct a theory of the physical universe) in which Man figures logically as no more than a new genus or family. It is an error of perspective which defaces and degrades the universal Phenomenon. In order to assign Man the place in nature which he deserves, it is not enough to extend the boundaries of classification by the addition of a supplementary section—not even by one additional order or branch.... The appearance of man, despite the insignificant anatomical advance involved, inaugurates a new age. The earth 'grows a new skin'. And better still, she finds her soul."[1]

[1] *Op. cit.,* p. 201.

SELECT BIBLIOGRAPHY

(An asterisk denotes works by non-Catholics)

Cosmogonies:

KARRER, O.: *Religions of Mankind*, trans. E. I. Watkin, London and New York, Sheed and Ward, 1936.

*SCHEBESTA, P.: *Among Congo Pygmies*, London, Hutchinson, 1937.

SCHMIDT, W.: *The Origin and Growth of Religion*, London, Methuen, 1931; *High Gods in North America*, Oxford, Clarendon Press, 1933.

*WILLIAMSON, R. W.: *Religion and Cosmic Beliefs of Central Polynesia*, two volumes, London and New York, Cambridge University Press, 1933.

Ancient Philosophies:

COPLESTON, Frederick C., S.J.: *A History of Philosophy*, six volumes, London, Burns Oates, and Westminster, Maryland, Newman Press, 1946–.

ARMSTRONG, A. H.: *An Introduction to Ancient Philosophy*, London, Methuen, 1947, and Westminster, Maryland, Newman Press, 1949.

Scientific Studies on Human Origins:

*MACCURDY, G. G.: *Early Man*, Philadelphia, Lippincott, 1937.

*LE GROS CLARK, W. E.: *Early Forerunners of Man*, Baltimore, 1934.

*BURKITT, M. C.: Prehistory, London and New York, Cambridge University Press, 1925.

28930

Theology and the question of Human Origins:

MESSENGER, E. C.: *Evolution and Theology*, London, Burns Oates, 1931 and Westminster, Maryland, Newman Press.

BIVORT DE LA SAUDÉE, Jacques de (Ed.): *God, Man and the Universe*, London, Burns Oates, and New York, Kenedy 1954. (This volume contains essays on scientific, philosophical and theological aspects of human origins together with useful bibliographies.)

TERNANT, Philip de: *Some Pathfinders in Organic Evolution*. London, Burns Oates, 1928.

MONRO, MARGARET T.: *Thinking about Genesis*, London and New York, Longmans, 1953.